The Hand and The Spirit: Religious Art in America 1700–1900

W9-DEZ-955

The Hand and The Spirit:
Religious Art
in America 1700–1900

Jane Dillenberger and Joshua C. Taylor

Schedule of the Exhibition

University Art Museum, Berkeley
June 28–August 27, 1972

National Collection of Fine Arts, Washington, D.C.
September 29–November 5, 1972

Dallas Museum of Fine Arts
December 10–January 14, 1972–1973

Indianapolis Museum of Art
February 20–April 15, 1973

Exhibition sponsored by
Graduate Theological Union, Berkeley
University Art Museum, Berkeley
National Collection of Fine Arts,
Smithsonian Institution, Washington, D.C.

This project is supported by grants from:
The National Endowment for the Arts in Washington, D.C.,
a Federal agency created by Act of Congress in 1965;
The Rockefeller Foundation, New York City;
The Lilly Endowment, Inc., Indianapolis, Indiana.

Published by University Art Museum, Berkeley, 1972.
All rights reserved.
Library of Congress card catalogue number 70–189052.

Table of Contents

Foreword

Peter Selz
Director, University Art Museum, Berkeley

"The Hand and The Spirit" is the result of the collaboration of many individuals and several institutions, and has been made possible by the enthusiastic support of all these disparate groups. When Jane Dillenberger came to me with her idea for this exhibition, I thought it represented a rare opportunity to originate a show of both scholarly significance and unusual public appeal. Yet, by virtue of the vast scope and proposed quality of the show, it seemed impossible for one museum to assume the task, both administratively and financially.

We set out to find a broader base of support which would enable us to realize this exciting project. We feel fortunate to have succeeded in this endeavor, and now to see the exhibition come to form in its fullest excellence. I want to express my gratitude, therefore, especially to our fellow sponsors of the exhibition, the Graduate Theological Union in Berkeley (and in particular to John Dillenberger, then President of the Theological Union, whose efforts on behalf of the exhibition were considerable) and the National Collection of Fine Arts, Smithsonian Institution, Washington, D.C. (and to the National Collection's Director, Joshua C. Taylor, who not only worked toward realization of the project, but also contributed to the text of the accompanying publication).

We are also very grateful for the foundation support we received, without which we could not have funded adequately either the exhibition or the publication: The Rockefeller Foundation, The Lilly Endowment, Inc., and the National Endowment for the Arts.

I am pleased, too, at the fine circulation we have for the exhibition, and I want to thank the directors and staffs of the Dallas Museum of Fine Arts and the Indianapolis Museum of Art for their cooperation in this regard.

Our most heartfelt thanks of course go to Jane Dillenberger, who has worked full-time for almost three years with enthusiastic devotion to make visible her idea that a genuine and thorough tradition of religious art did in fact exist in America of the eighteenth and nineteenth centuries. Everyone who sees this exhibition will benefit from her passionate involvement in the project.

There were many individuals who gave of their time and energy to assist us with this exhibition, and I would like to join Jane in her thanks to these many people (see p. 7 of catalogue).

Preface and Acknowledgments

Jane Dillenberger

Guest Director of the Exhibition
for the University Art Museum, Berkeley
Associate Professor, Theology and the
Arts, Graduate Theological Union, Berkeley

After teaching the history of continental religious art to theological students for two decades, what started as a diversionary study of Eakins' art drew me into the American field and finally into an intensive search for American art with Biblical or religious subject matter. The search, involving the subterranean storage areas of most of the major museums in this country, yielded large numbers of painting and sculpture. It was clear that an exhibition of a selection of these would be fascinating and instructive, providing us with fresh clues to both American art and religion.

Conversations with Peter Selz, Director of the University Art Museum, Berkeley, and with my husband, John Dillenberger, then head of Berkeley's Graduate Theological Union, met with such interest that agreements resulted for joint sponsorship of an exhibition by both institutions. In the meantime, some of the research problems in regard to the artist William Page led me to Joshua Taylor, whose definitive book on Page had been so helpful. My inquiries came to his desk in his first months as Director of the National Collection of Fine Arts, Washington, D.C. He had been thinking of the same theme for an exhibition sponsored by the National Collection, both because of his own interest and because the National Collection owns extraordinarily fine works in the field, such as the superb Ryder, "Jonah," and LaFarge's "Jesus and Nicodemus." The result was the happy addition of the National Collection of Fine Arts as an exhibition sponsor, followed later by two subscribers, the Dallas Museum of Fine Arts and the Indianapolis Museum of Art.

Most important, Joshua Taylor became a continuing consultant and co-worker. Together we shaped the exhibition by the choice of the works of art, and together we arranged the particular groupings found in this catalogue. It was Joshua Taylor who suggested the felicitous title, *The Hand and The Spirit.* Working with him has been a delightful, stimulating, and instructive experience. Dr. Lois Fink assisted Dr. Taylor in searching out some of the data used in his essay.

Alfred Frankenstein, Curator of American Art at the University Art Museum, Berkeley, and author of many important articles and books in the field, has also been a mentor, providing out-of-the-way nuggets of information, querying my viewpoint and materials in a helpful way. I thank him for his enthusiasm and interest. These latter qualities have also characterized my many associations with Brenda Richardson, Assistant Director for Exhibitions, and Joy Feinberg, Registrar, from the University Art Museum. They have handled a multiplicity of problems with ease, efficiency, and good humor.

My husband has been a companion in sleuthing out works of art from Vermont to California, and Oregon to Georgia. He has also served as photographer, editorial assistant, and contributor. Through the more than two years of intensive work, he too read extensively in the field, and became a resource for information and the testing of ideas. Since his resignation from the presidency of, to teaching in, the Graduate Theological Union, I have had more access to his own resources.

The research and the exhibition itself have been made possible by three grants. The University Art Museum, Berkeley, received a grant from the National Endowment for the Arts to assist them in the special work of preparing the exhibition from the standpoint of the Museum. Two grants have particularly assisted me. The Rockefeller Foundation, through a two-year grant to the University of California, Berkeley, has assisted in my travel and research expenses. The Lilly Endowment, Inc., through a grant to the Graduate Theological Union, assisted in providing funds for the conservation of several works of art which could not otherwise have been loaned to the exhibition, and made possible a more generously illustrated and documented catalogue. The exhibition could not have been assembled on the basis of information available in libraries, even those of museums, however excellent they may be in the American field. Hence, travel was of key importance. The illustrated, documented catalogue will remain after the exhibition ends its tour and works of art have been returned to their many owners. It is for these reasons that I feel a particular sense of gratitude to the officials of the Rockefeller Foundation and to the Lilly Endowment, Inc.

Finally, I want to thank the many lenders to the exhibition, without whose complete and generous cooperation the show would not have been possible. We had success in requesting loans from a multitude of public and private collections in this country, despite the fact that very often our requests were for works of art of great value and fragility which travel infrequently. The names of individual institutions and collectors who loaned to the exhibition are on p.188 of this catalogue.

Introduction

John Dillenberger

Professor of Historical Theology
Graduate Theological Union, Berkeley

Most American church historians have dealt with the theme of American destiny, that is, with the religious understanding and self-understanding of the nation. There can be no doubt about the importance of this theme from the founding of New England through the settling of the West to our moral posture as a nation in the world.

By contrast, the relation of religious currents and traditions to the arts, particularly painting and sculpture, has received scant attention, usually with the assumption by both art and church historians that there is little material and even less mutual influence. This exhibition and its research as Alfred Frankenstein has pointed out, disclose that American religious painting and sculpture exist in quantity. Moreover, these works of art are neither so ephemeral nor so peripheral as to warrant the apparent inattention. Indeed, the inattention says more about our historic interests and perceptions than about the significance of the materials at the time they were executed.

This situation calls for the necessity and urgency of mutual and collaborative research from the side of art and church historians. Otherwise, the works of art will themselves continue in neglect, with further physical deterioration. If that should continue, the sample of data will be so partial that the lack of evidence will forever destroy the possibility of an accurate picture of our heritage.

There are many references by the artists themselves to associations with churchmen, theologians, and church traditions that are explicit and provide another kind of evidence than what is communicated by their paintings, as the text of this catalogue shows. Travel diaries of the nineteenth century frequently, too, record the associations between the two groups, indicating that the contemporaries of the artists did discern connections we no longer see.

From the side of the church, attention has focused on the popular use of art, without scholarly attention to the transcending moments of the conjunction of significant art and religious perception. So here, too, there is an hiatus.

There is a past to be uncovered and reappropriated. It is my own conviction that the full exploration of the interrelations will take us far beyond the specific connections now established and partially explored. For some artists, the new intoxication with nature, fostered by science and theology and made mani-

fest in the abundant nature of America, created a new perception and a new content. On the opposite end, are such circumscribed developments as Shaker art, Pennsylvania frakturs, and the New Mexican santos, in which an intensity of religious perception was joined to indigenous materials resulting in a particular style appropriate to express a specific outlook.

But both the preoccupation with nature and the specific development within the traditions just noted leave out a broad spectrum of art and religious understanding in America. This exhibition includes much such central material, for which the research and interpretation is much less advanced. Indeed, this material may stand near to the central religious tradition and its neglect may explain in part the lack of sustained interest on the part of the church in such painting and sculpture.

What is called for is a comprehensive analysis and interpretation, a discerning perception based on research yet to be done. The research for this exhibition has exposed a veritable flood of material, of which this selection is only a small fraction. From my own experience in traveling with Jane to many museums, I can testify to the neglect and "basement storage" category to which some of these paintings have been assigned. In recent reading and research in American religious history, I too am seeing aspects of interrelations which we have largely passed by. Seldom is the invitation for new work so alluring or promising.

The Hand and The Spirit

Joshua C. Taylor

Joshua C. Taylor

Director, National Collection of Fine Arts,
Smithsonian Institution, Washington, D.C.

The Religious Impulse

To those who have a general knowledge of art produced during the eighteenth and early nineteenth centuries in the area of the United States, it comes as no surprise that exhibition records list few locally produced works with titles that mark them as serving religious purpose. Such a fact is rather taken for granted. Yet were one to think of the extensive preoccupation with religion throughout the same period, of the extraordinary bulk of sermons and theological writing in the hands of society, the question might well arise why this should be so. Can it be that art grew untouched by either the will to new theologies or the pursuit of religious "enthusiasm" of the time?

To suppose that this lack of obvious religiosity in art is simply the result of a largely protestant culture, is too easy an answer. Although the nature of the church in America in its diversified forms allowed for little direct patronage of art, there was nothing in protestant thought that would militate against art as such; most movements, whether philosophical or evangelical in spirit, insisted that a religious principle must underlie all human activity, and given the fact that art did exist, one might suppose that it was granted no exception. In fact, to judge from early discourses on art and from the writings of many artists—although by no means all—the artistic elements of society were no less moved by religious zeal than were the preachers of fire and brimstone and the founders of utopian communities.

"Religious faith," wrote a commentator in 1854, "is an essential element in true art." "Here is a nation distinguished above all other nations for religiosity and for freedom," said George Bancroft in 1863, echoing much earlier sentiments, "and, therefore, here, above all other nations, is art destined to achieve its greatest triumph."

It is notable that in America the clergy often felt called upon to discuss art of all kinds; art was part of the clergyman's realm. Sometimes, as with the Rev. Bethune, the clergyman could speak with knowledge and authority. Sometimes he was called on simply to testify to the purity of undraped sculpture. In a rather uncritical way, the beauty of art was usually linked to an indeterminate good, and the keepers of the good were often the judges of the true and the artistically valid.

Art of religious inspiration, to be sure, must not be looked upon as being of a single kind. "Religious art" through this period might refer to art that falls into one of three very generally defined categories. In one class might be grouped depictions of Biblical scenes and characters, paintings related to ecclesiastical practice, and homiletic or moral depictions ranging from the gentle paintings of Thomas Hicks to scenes of pious family life. Also in this class would be numbered the widely circulated popular prints, usually of sentimental persuasion, that vividly capitalized on evangelical imagery. All of these can be called religious because of their obvious association with a sect or with religious literature. A more complex category, more difficult to define, is that including works which express their religious motivation through their deliberate choice of style or aesthetic formulation. The close association at times between the moral and aesthetic vocabulary is of some significance in this regard. Then in a class by itself is that major movement in American painting in which nature was treated in such a fashion as to transform a landscape view into a religious experience, sometimes overtly, sometimes by philosophical inference. It would be difficult to argue that any one of these categories can more legitimately be called "religious" than another, particularly considering the changes that the term "religious" underwent in the nineteenth century. That religious thought could be so diversely expressed is the important fact.

As an isolated term, "religious art," then, is basically meaningless and might even be considered, by such as Croce, false and misleading. Although in discussing the art of an earlier moment in history, historians have been content to call the art allied with the church and its traditions "religious," changes in art and thought took place in the late eighteenth century that quite complicate such a simple association. For one thing, traditional concepts of religion changed under the scrutiny of new scientific inquiry. As a result, much traditional imagery, for various reasons, began to lose its ecclesiastical substance; it could no longer be assumed to play its traditional role in the practices of the church. However, although the analytical efforts expended on historical and scientific inquiry might very well have stood against all religious dogma unequivocally, they were not necessarily anti-religious or antithetic to mystical revelation. Emanuel Swedenborg was only one example of a man who could be at once a religious visionary and a man of science.

The desire was to find a "true" religion, one that took into account all that was known scientifically of man and the earth in all possible diversity. The preoccupation was apparent in an extraordinary range of studies, from geology to linguistics, and the wide-ranging extension of religious concern was not over-looked by the visual arts. But a cosmic rather than an ecclesiastical sense of order became the unifying principle of the new knowledge, and when Biblical matter was considered, it was often presented as the symbol of a larger conception, if not simply as a fact in the systematic study of human history. Biblical subject matter did not necessarily refer to religion in any traditional sense. Classical idealism and Christian morality were freely blended; Greek heroes and Christian saints could be seen by some as manifestations of a similar cosmic impulse; and each new discovery of a land or people could be fitted into the great puzzle through which the mind of God was newly, and more completely, made manifest to human kind.

Underlying the efforts through the early nineteenth century to find an ultimate spiritual truth within the complexity of modern knowledge, was an impressive capacity to sustain an abstraction, a principle of thought or form common to all pursuits. In the visual arts this became, in a sometimes simplistic way, a belief in a kind of universal primal form, which was described as a formal configuration that has an immediate and intuitively grasped meaning for the mind. The interpretation of "meaning" might vary widely, but it tended always to relate the individual perceiver to a spiritual source. Thus, the work of art, both in its means and its ends, was clearly separated from a simple vision of nature; removed from the transient environment of casual observation, it became a sensuous object that was at the same time an object of thought. A new study, which was called "aesthetic," undertook to describe meaning in terms of an identity between perception and mind or, in some cases, perception and spiritual knowledge.

Ironically, in view of later ideas that based spiritual manifestations wholly on peculiarly individual revelation, in America this concern for meaningful form first took on substance through the dogmatic teaching of Sir Joshua Reynolds. The introduction of the concept of high style supported by his writings was a major step in the spiritual justification of art in America, in its demanding a place in the culture on moral,

ethical and even theological grounds.

The new theological concerns, then, were made evident less in the subject matter than in the form of presentation, because all subject matter could be seen as part of a theological whole. "It is the perception and adoption into ourselves of the highest truth which makes the religious man or artist," wrote a critic of Ruskinian persuasion in 1855, "a matter which concerns the heart equally with the intellect, while this acceptation of dogma [as in modern French treatment of religious subjects] is but a cold, intellectual action, having no vital influence on the life or the picture..." This does not mean, of course, that all paintings of the period, regardless of subject, are to be interpreted as manifestations of theological impulse; the thought of the rampant iconological homiletics that such an assumption could produce is frightening. It means simply that if one looks with care, with the proper religious sensibility, he may see that some art which makes no commitment as to subject, may have served in the minds of the pious artist and his sympathetic following, a spiritual need and a religious end.

It would be tempting to cite as background for art in the United States the rich mass of theologically-colored artistic theory of late eighteenth and early nineteenth century Europe, the writings of Herder and Tieck and Wackenroder, or the concerns of Ottley, Chateaubriand or Séroux D'Agincourt for example, but there is little evidence that American artists, with one or two notable exceptions, initially had direct contact with their theories or were prepared to follow the niceties of their arguments. When, by the 1840s, theological assumptions and a transcendental vocabulary began to appear with frequency in the statements of artists and critics in America, they had become almost commonplaces and need have had no single direct source. American ties between religion and art tended to spring from rather humbler sources. Although William Blake in England and the Friedrich Overbeck circle in Rome reacted strongly against academic theory and leaned heavily on new theological and philosophical concerns, the American painters and sculptors early in the century looked upon the academic abstract standards of form as a salvation from the mundane concerns of portraiture and utilitarian job work. So-called classical taste lingered in America far longer than in many European countries because it was associated not only with elevation and genius but with Christian good.

For the most part, artists based their aesthetic arguments on the *Discourses* of Reynolds and took their matching theology directly from the pulpit. To artists trying to make themselves a place in a culture with little artistic tradition, the words of Reynolds meant something very different from what they meant to painters brought up in the discipline of the European schools. The words "good," "high," and "beautiful" had a special meaning in the context of American preaching; Reynolds, with his emphasis on industry, his disparagement of sensuality and his persistent exhortation to "rise above," sounded like an artist prophet pointing toward salvation. As late as 1826, when the artists who had formed themselves into a group that was to become the National Academy wished to give prizes to successful students, a specially bound copy of the *Discourses* was awarded; and the practice continued for many years.

It is not that there was a notable lack of art devoted to traditional religious subject matter in Eastern America at the beginning of the nineteenth century; every collection and exhibition boasted such works. But they were almost all "old masters" or copies of older works. Of course it would have been difficult to profess a love of past art without accepting religious subjects, and so great was the desire on the part of collectors to possess the traditional images of art, that most young painters paid their way abroad by agreeing to make copies of works in Italian and French collections. In the early works of many painters, Copley, Trumbull, Robert Weir, for example, religious subjects do appear, but their appearance probably has more to do with an effort to establish links with the traditions of art than to promote the traditions of religion. So long as the subject was infused with an Old World feeling, evoking a kind of nostalgia for someone else's past, it was acceptable. A Raphaelesque Madonna, a Saint Jerome after Domenichino, a Holy Family by Andrea del Sarto were considered morally rewarding, not because of the significance of their subjects but because of their appeal as art.

The piety expressed in art itself extended in a curious way to make acceptable the religious practices of "artistic" countries abroad, notably Italy. While the largely protestant group of Americans going to Italy was well braced against the blandishments of Catholic practice, their letters home show a strange ambivalence. Long passages are devoted to sentimental descriptions of peasants at prayer, church pageantry or the quiet of cloisters, only to be followed by criticism and disclaimers. So staunch a Protestant as Morse was moved to ruminate about the problems of life in viewing in 1830 the often depicted wayside shrine at Subiaco which he promptly painted, later turning his study into an overtly religious scene with a kneeling peasant and inspirational light. Like most visiting Americans, Robert W. Weir attended the service of a novice taking her vows and was stirred to paint the scene in 1826, emphasizing the pomp and elegance as well as the pathos. Granet's interior of the Capuchin church was immediately hailed by Americans and much admired, not only for its spectacular effect of radiating light, but because of the holy quiet of its atmosphere.

Yet for all their interest in religious practices abroad, American artists seem rarely to have turned their attention to depicting religious happenings at home except for an occasional family scene with a Bible or a former slave reading the Bible to a child. A special kind of pietistic sentiment allowed art to bridge sectarian gaps, but not to ally itself with local religious activity. Elevation could be achieved through remoteness of style or remoteness of place; there seemed to be little concern for direct spiritual transport.

Biblical subject matter, divorced from the sentiment of past masters of art, was maintained in the eastern colonies and states more on a popular level than on the level of "high" art. Beginning with such works as the remarkable paintings by as yet anonymous painters from the Albany area, based largely on engraved illustrations, a kind of domestic tradition persisted, carried on through imported prints, watercolors and even embroideries. Rather than being in themselves expressions of religious zeal, they are pious testimonials to a given religious practice and accepted belief. Their charm is in their fanciful embellishment of the subject.

There was, of course, a totally different attitude toward Biblical and liturgical themes in the extensive area of the Southwest that developed as a part of Mexico, an outpost of the rich Spanish tradition. It is only in this region that an intense religious passion shaped the given forms with a new and powerful expression. Only in this area, too, was the religious sense of the indigenous peoples incorporated into the European tradi-

Samuel F. B. Morse (1791–1872). *Chapel of the Virgin at Subiaco.*
(Completed January of 1831). Oil on canvas. 29-15/16 x 37″. Worcester
Art Museum, Worcester, Massachusetts: Bequest of Stephen Salisbury
III. [Not in exhibition].

tion to create a fresh and distinctive art. It is significant, however, that when this area was annexed to the United States and was gradually engulfed by the westward movement, the existing art was simply ignored. At a later point, the mission architecture was noted by painters hungry for new scenes, but was treated with the same sentimental gloss as the wayside chapels of Italy. An appreciation of the seriousness and poignancy of the art itself came only with a shift in artistic and cultural values in the present century.

The monasteries and religious centers throughout the Mississippi valley followed in general a very different pattern. With few exceptions, the art that adorned the churches was brought from Europe or was created to reflect as closely as possible the traditional models. Although it occasionally reflected the new Purist art of the Church in Rome, it more often looked backward to earlier models. It seems to have had no impact at all on the art of the salons or galleries, nor on public imagery outside of its immediate circle.

The many separate religious sects that were established in the early nineteenth century seem to have cared little for the figurative arts. Although their teaching is rich with imagery, this was not translated into visual expression. The frenzy and ecstasy of a camp meeting were abetted by hypnotic music and poetic fervor, but never attached themselves to painterly activity. And this is noteworthy, since an art of exuberance was the subject of much discussion in Europe during these years. It simply did not occur to the artists or their critics that this kind of transport was either possible or desirable in the visual arts.

The best art could do for a movement such as that of the Mormons, was to record its history, the exterior manisfestation of a religion, not its spiritual center. Only the Swedenborgian teaching had a direct impact on art, and this was through its link with a complex philosophical view of perception and aesthetic judgment which suggested not narrative themes but a spiritual context for artistic form.

Spirit and Form

Possibly the rather special interpretation in the United States given to the ideas expressed in the *Discourses* of Reynolds owes most to the work and personality of Washington Allston. He was the most important and quite probably the first American artist consciously to equate spirit and form, and became the living embodiment of the spiritual artist to a whole generation of aspiring painters. To be sure, he took much of his early inspiration from Benjamin West, but West seems not to have communicated these qualities to others of his American pupils, nor to have projected the ideas underlying the turbulent imagery of some of his late paintings. It was Allston, steeped in the theories of his friend Coleridge and the associational principles of such theorists as Archibald Alison, and aware as well of the ideas of his German contemporaries, who made clear to his associates that art was the great mediator between spirit and matter, freeing the sensuous from its earthly bonds. Devoted to the ideal, he was no more classical in his understanding of the term than was Kant, whose philosophy he in some ways reflects. Harmonious beauty is a quality of mind, of apprehension, not of the object. Divorced from the physical limitations of the thing, it exists in a realm of "moral purity and religious devotion." In following the variety of form apparent within the incorruptible unity of a painting by Raphael he wrote:

> I feel the pleasurable, full control
> Of Grace, harmonious, boundless and intense.

But he carefully demonstrated that the same sense of harmony was to be found in the underlying structure of an Ostade as it was in a Raphael. Although the coarseness or grossly secular nature of the subject might intrude, the real content of the work of art is the sense of perfection kindled in the imagination by the persuasive forms, proved true in the harmonious pleasure of the individual mind.

To call this sense of exalted, peaceful harmony religious is hardly to agree with the stern doctrine of original sin and predestination colorfully set forth in the revival movements of the eighteenth century which continued in exaggerated form through much of the nineteenth. But it does indeed agree with the growing Unitarian sense preached by Ellery Channing and with the later system put forth suggestively by Emerson and the Concord circle. Art, if not itself an expression of religion, was a means to the universal religious experience. In good Herbartian fashion, the senses, harmonized by the sensitive understanding of the artist, could teach the mind of the beholder to grasp the essential order of the universal mind.

Probably it was from this belief in the work of art's existing in the still moment when external form and internal feeling coalesce, that reverie became a close associate of the artistic experience. Art provided the means for living the dream of perfection. Allston's sitters are rarely present to the viewer in any tangible sense; they are convincingly solid and sensuously whole, but seem to live not because they are capable of external motion but because they are quietly in contact with an internal voice. They are always listening. If there is no figure with whom the viewer can identify himself, the landscape itself invites reverie, a lapse through a waking dream into an inner world of calm and security. Although Allston delighted in Radcliffian horror, his dream does not share with Goya the terror of the irrational. Reverie is a joining with the uninterrupted harmony of timeless, tranquil being.

When American sculptors first reached Italy, which they considered the home of artistic reverie, they found there, as had Allston, a movement among the artists not foreign in its principles to their own idealism. To call either Horatio Greenough or Hiram Powers simply "classical" or "neo-classical" is to miss the point of their efforts. Although Greenough believed heartily in his functional aesthetic, which was the foundation of much late eighteenth-century theory, whether the poetical rules of Marmontel or their parody applied to architecture and painting by Milizia, he linked it inseparably to his perceptual, natural world. He saw every natural phenomenon as the working out of an active universal principle, and the great works of the past served only as keys to unlock the secret recesses of this underlying meaning. If the austere composition of his statue of Washington recalls the Olympian Zeus, it was not to identify Washington with a god, but to demonstrate that the underlying form that communicates a sense of justice, firmness and grandeur directly to the mind—at least to minds which are prepared for such communication—distinguishes them both. The search for the simplest, thus most universal, meaningful form in nature was the goal of many artists gathered in Italy during the first half of the century. Their efforts were called "purist" because they tried to match exactly and flawlessly the outer form with the inner content, and the inner content was ultimately the intimation of God.

Hiram Powers was of particular importance in the projection of this purist image. On one hand as literal and down to earth as might befit a proper Yankee, he reflected in his work both the fleshly aspect of Bartolini and the rather austere imagery of Thorwaldsen and Tenerani. Yet once he had settled in Italy he turned to ideal subjects such as *Eve* and *The Greek Slave* and gave them a special overtone of meaning. Although his *Eve Tempted* might also be a Venus gloating over her prize, there is a quality of observation, a softness and fleshly specificity within the disciplined harmony of the enclosing form that removes her from the realm of goddesses. Her remoteness is less a matter of formal abstraction than a sense of inwardness, of fleshly existence caught in the perfect web of stilling thought. Ideality, in other words, is a state of mind not a complex of bodily measurements. And this state of mind must be developed with full knowledge of candidly observed physical fact. It is revealing that Powers became an active member of the Swedenborgian group in Florence, sufficiently dedicated to convince others of the doctrine's importance for art.

The writing of Emanuel Swedenborg fit into American artistic thought at this time in a remarkable way. For Swedenborg, every man carried within himself the potentiality for existing in heaven or hell. Hell was the disruption of the harmonious functioning of the universe. But harmony for Swedenborg was not simply the balancing of external forms; it was the perfect coordinations of qualities he termed the Divine Love and the Divine Wisdom in the constantly evolving universe. The extraordinary appeal of his doctrine was his principle that the two divine qualities were basic to both the spiritual and the material spheres of action. What our physical eye sees is a correspondence in the physical world of time and space of what we can know by insight of the spiritual world, which is measured in moral dimensions. During our earthly existence we live in both worlds simultaneously, or rather, our world has both a spiritual and a physical dimension. He went so far as to point out that the development of the human being from conception to maturity through the interaction of the heart and the respiratory system, is the physical manifestation of the moral development of man through the interaction of Divine Love and Wisdom.

For the artist devoted to creating a realm of pure thought, of ideality, but keenly aware also of the ever more complex visible world around him, Swedenborg's concept of correspondence provided a possible means by which matter could be elevated to the realm of spirit. He was challenged to see within each new natural complexity to come to his attention the principle of spiritual order, not abstractable in a system of form but existing as a harmonious process. Once imbued with this vision, the artist could recognize the limiting nature of external form as compared to the freedom of spiritual form, and attempt to catch those perfect moments when a physical manifestation gives way to spiritual awareness. The Transfiguration on the Mount was the perfect example of a moment in which the corporeal aspect of man was suddenly seen in its spiritual context. But the Transfiguration was seen only by those who had learned to see, to recognize man's dual existence. Each work of art should, in its way, be a kind of transfiguration.

William Page, who discovered Swedenborg through Powers, carried the theory further in artistic practice. He insisted that even the work of art itself should clearly achieve its outer form as result of an inner process, like that of nature. Painting his shadowy pictures in carefully superimposed layers of paint, he wished the viewer to look into them, quite literally, to make contact with a process of life. This is the way he looked at the paintings of Titian, which he considered equivalent to the works of nature itself. He did not think of color as evocative in the usual sense, not as a harmony of hues, but rather as a means for setting up an interplay of forces within the substance of the painting suggesting a depth of activity extending well beyond what the physical eye could see. The viewer could then engage in a process of formation and becoming that corresponds to the harmonious interaction of the universal qualities of heart and mind. A person who learns to see in this way, said Page, can never feel alone; simply looking with care about him he can feel himself to be always a part of a live and spiritual world.

There has been much speculation on whether the later paintings of George Inness, who was introduced to Swedenborg by Page, are indeed a reflection of these mystical ideas. Inness had always been concerned with religious values and this would seem a logical extension. Actually, a softening in effect began to invade much of American painting from the late 1860s on. Pictorially the technique doubtless owes much to the French painters of Barbizon. But the content for Inness is not the same. The desire for identification with the peasant, with the sweet-

ness of toil, evident in the works of many, including Americans, who looked toward Barbizon for inspiration, plays only a fleeting role in the work of Inness. More and more the actual objects of nature become only motifs for the expression of an inner mystery, invitations for speculation and reverie. His autumn sunsets of the 1870s are treatises neither on observed phenomena nor on the sentimental implications of nature's cycles; they are studies in shifting color and form that provide haunting moments in which the mind is encouraged to discover the spiritual counterpart of matter, to seek release from limiting time and space. Objects are only punctuation marks in the evanescent atmosphere of thought. If this was not prompted by Swedenborg, it nonetheless can be understood in Swedenborgian terms.

The success of Inness' later painting suggests that at least some among the knowledgeable public were ready to accept art as an invitation to reflection rather than a proof of concrete matter and pragmatic skill. But the language, which owes so much to Hunt and the painters of Barbizon, should not be confused with the ultimate content. Vagueness and a crepuscular atmosphere do not in themselves prove a spiritual impulse. It is the depth of personal but selfless involvement that places Inness, and such painters as Robert Loftin Newman, among the painters of the spiritual ideal.

Sermons in Stones

At what point American landscape and the rural scene became identified with godliness and superior virtue is hard to determine, but in painting surely it was Thomas Cole who most emphatically brought the association to the public consciousness. He belongs to a long line of artists beginning in the eighteenth century who were devoted to the discovery of the sublime and the picturesque. The concepts of Burke were still very much alive in early nineteenth-century America; the satires on the picturesque of "Dr. Syntax" had little effect on American thought. In fact it was only in the 1820s that painters and architects began to take seriously the ideas of sublimity in natural scenery and consider the relationship between landscape and mind. In a touching reference to the eighteenth-century Englishman's fascination with cascades, the Quaker, Edward Hicks, painstakingly printed around the frame of his 1825 view of Niagara Falls some lines from Alexander Wilson's "The For-

Hiram Powers (1805–1873). *Eve Tempted.* (1839). Marble.
National Collection of Fine Arts, Smithsonian Institution, Washington, D.C.:
Purchased in memory of Ralph Cross Johnson. [Not in exhibition].

esters" of 1809:

> This great o'erwhelming work of awful time,
> In all its dread magnificence sublime,
> Rises on our view, amid a crashing roar
> That bids us kneel, and Time's great God adore.

William Cullen Bryant was afraid that Cole would lose his spiritual sense of landscape when he went to Europe in 1829, finding there

> . . . everywhere the trace of men,
> Paths, homes, graves, ruins . . .

Yet, in fact, Cole seems always to have looked upon landscape less as evocation than as human parable; he was far less devoted to the selfless view of nature than Bryant would have one believe. He identified himself with a strong religious strain in American culture that was far grimmer than the deistic optimism of Bryant. His delight in terror and the overwhelming, in the destructive force of nature with its promise of salvation only after earthly storms, places him quite opposite to Allston with his serene and benign sense of natural order. Although Cole was an indefatigable student of natural form and effect and enjoyed losing himself in the wilds, he was basically a histrionic painter. Rarely if ever do his landscapes reflect a general state of cerebral and cosmic unity, but instead act out a passionate struggle between good and evil, life and death, salvation and damnation. As in a sermon by Jonathan Edwards, God is both a threat and a promise, and nature dramatically presents the lesson to man ". . . poor pilgrims, on this darkling sphere. . . ." Cole more nearly approaches an expression of the doctrine of predestination than any other major American painter. In spite of Bryant's interpretation of his work in nationalistic terms, seeing his wild nature as peculiarly American, Cole was always first a moralistic artist who painted nature as the expression of a personal drama. In Italy in 1830, where most landscapists were devoted to a new vision of clear forms and natural light, Cole saw everything with the penumbra of moral and historical sentiment. Even in the drawing of a single tree, Cole dramatized the rhythm of its growth to give it human meaning. Although his notebooks abound in nice observations on atmosphere and topography, in painting his vision was not separate from his gesture. That in his late years Cole turned almost wholly to paintings on religious and moral themes is not sur-

prising; the major change was that his language, at first drawn from natural forms, often anthropomorphized, became more directly expressive. In 1842 he joined the Anglican church in a kind of confirmation of his pictorial homiletics.

A significant difference separates Cole from those who cited him as their inspiration in landscape painting. While he had felt called upon to translate his experiences of nature into dramatically framed sermons, the growing school of landscapists accepted the fact that nature had spiritual value in itself and felt less and less the need to emphasize the fact in their paintings. They had outgrown the distinctions of the sublime and the beautiful as provoking particular responses and looked upon nature in all of its aspects as imbuing the men who associated with it with godly qualities. Nor was this a matter of formal suggestion. "A majestic landscape," remarked E. L. Magoon in an essay, "Scenery and Mind," published in 1852, "often scanned and truly loved, imparts much of its greatness to the mind and heart of the spectator." Furthermore, he noted, "In viewing magnificent scenes, the soul, expanded and sublimed, is imbued with a spirit of divinity, and appears, as it were, associated with the Deity himself." It is not, then, for the artist to interpret or express, but simply to respond to nature's attractions and record what he sees, to bring the magnificent vision into the compass of the drawing room. At most, as Emerson said in an unfortunate phrase, art might provide the gymnastics of the eye, preparing the observer to recognize and respond to the real thing.

Although Cole preferred to disparage art in favor of nature, his works are overtly artful, even by contemporary standards. But as Asher Brown Durand, for example, progressed in his career, the artful structure and the gestural form tended to give way in his work to an art of direct perception. Yet to read Durand's commentaries on art is to be aware that the motivation was nonetheless religious. The burden of religiosity, however, was carried by a pre-existing assumption about nature, not by narrative or an engaging formal expressiveness. Bryant's famous opening lines to Thanatopsis:

> To him who in the love of nature holds
> Communion with her visible forms, she speaks
> A various language . . .

effectively excludes the person who comes to nature unpre-

Edward Hicks (1780–1849). *The Falls of Niagara.* Oil on canvas. 31½ x
38″. The Metropolitan Museum of Art, New York: Gift of Edgar William and Bernice Chrysler Garbisch, 1962. [Not in exhibition].

pared. Similarly, the paintings of most landscapists grouped loosely as a Hudson River School, are religious only insofar as the observer accepts the principle that an intensive view of nature constitutes a religious experience, that he recognizes a closeness to nature as a closeness to God. As in the works of some of the followers of Ruskin in England, there was no observable relationship between the religious impulse and the artistic result; not unlike many non-figurative paintings of the early twentieth century which provide no internal clues for the interpretation of the responses they provoke, the exacting views of nature depended on a context of spirituality supplied by the prepared mind of the viewer. Possibly this explains the increase in writing about art by artists and their friends.

Ruskin's early writing in *Modern Painters* made perfect sense to those writers in the art periodical, *The Crayon*, in the 1850s who accepted the premise that art becomes spiritual in direct proportion to its ceasing to be art. And Ruskin was pleased because he felt that in America he had found "heartier appreciation and a better understanding" than he had ever met with in England.

In these same years, the 1860s and 1870s, the horizons of landscape were vastly expanded. The natural image available to the artist went well beyond even the most extravagant imagination of those who had found the Hudson or the White Mountains wild and magnificent. Frederic Edwin Church, who had studied with Cole and early painted a *Moses Viewing the Promised Land* and *Christian on the Borders of the Valley of Death,* left modest landscapes and Biblically related subject matter behind and sought more and more grandiose scenes as inspiration, as if requiring ever greater magnitude to keep alive the emotional and spiritual life Cole could detect in a ruined snag. Unafraid of an obsession with the material fact, he pursued visual novelty continuously, from the tropics of South America to the Arctic icebergs. Although his paintings have been described in terms of God and the creation, there is little to suggest that the thrill is other than one of discovery and amazement for their own sake, akin to the growing compulsion to collect exotic artifacts and amass unexpected remnants of strange cultures. Curiosity and a yen for exploration that allows judgment to be suspended in the joy of discovery, crowded out the religious premise which first made nature the key to a new American art.

Much the same can be said for the works of Albert Bierstadt, Thomas Moran and others continuing through the century. Yellowstone, Yosemite and the reaches of the West furnished heroic images that could satisfactorily substitute for moral passion or a spiritual humility of vision. Nature, gigantic nature, was there to be possessed by man.

Through all of this, religious language was retained in discussing the goals and means of landscape painting. The briefly active Society for the Advancement of Truth in Art, formed in 1863, rephrased the concepts of Godliness, however, in terms of Truth, and in painting they meant quite literally, truth to what is seen. Even Durand was considered a mannerist. Church was for the most part accepted, but Bierstadt was a false and exaggerating showman. Paintings, or for that matter architecture and furnishings, were as righteous as they were accurate and well defined, and demonstrated the Puritan virtue of selfless hard work, much as described under Ruskin's Lamp of Sacrifice. Grandeur was looked upon with some suspicion as being in league with vanity. A chaste aesthetic of functional nicety was for this reforming group synonymous with morality, with spiritual good, to the point that Clarence Cook, one of the founders of the Society, could refer to the design of a wash stand as "Sancta Simplicitas." For many painters by the 1860s, nature no longer was the embodiment of the mysterious source, but provided the means for proving the moral acuity of man.

Holiness and the Historical Sense

As if in reaction to the materialization of nature, there developed in the United States through the last quarter of the century a movement to bring art itself once more into direct association with spiritual meaning. It is noteworthy in this respect that even the English pre-Raphaelite group was divided between an exact depiction of things as they appeared and an alliance with the forms and spirit of past art. In America John LaFarge, in the early 1870s, turned his back on the literalness of Ruskin's teachings, once considered the basis of morality in art, and embraced the medieval sentiments of Rossetti and Morris. In a sense, the Rossettian aspect was the mode that now came to the fore in America.

With the growth of public art collections in the 1870s, the beginning of systematic instruction in the history of art, and the greater availability of earlier art through reproductions and easier travel, a whole new sense for art as it existed in the realm of masterpieces rather than in nature came into being. This new world of the spirit constructed out of art works from the past, demanded a concentration and sensibility quite out of the ordinary. Remote from mundane pursuits, it was well beyond the comprehension of vulgar minds, although a strong evangelical movement was launched on its behalf. This new ideality depended neither on nature nor on a single style but on the realization that there was such an entity as a world of art and that it could be considered synonymous with the world of the spirit. Accumulated works of art provided a link with the spiritual life of the past in such a way that one might even presume to live within the borders of art, escaping the limits of accelerated modern time and the extravagance of modern space. In this sensuous but curiously immaterial world, religion found a new expression.

The essential quality necessary for any work to join this special world was a subtle demand made by style or subject matter on a developed sense of connoisseurship. That is, the work must exist on at least two levels, that of its direct but understated sensuous appeal and that of historical reference available only to the cultured mind. The most conspicuous monument to this artistic spirituality was probably Richardson's Trinity Church in Boston, begun in 1874, in which the refinement of taste, both historical and artistic, was somehow equatable with the elect quality of the religious experience. Different from the rather simple, generalized expressiveness of the earlier gothic revival, this remarkable building brought forcibly home to the religious congregation, both the creative activity of artists, who themselves were regarded as spiritual leaders, and the satisfying remoteness of a mysterious but nicely defined past.

When John LaFarge, who earlier had believed that art was true, even in a moral sense, only when exactly imitating nature, turned his religiously motivated interests toward the medieval past to discover an art of personal statement, he was insisting that truth lay within the deeply seated individual experience, not in objective observation. Form again began to speak a spiritual language, but a language tuned not so much to a central ideality as to a private welling up of sentiment, the nostalgia for a knowledge known in the past and forgotten by the pres-

ent. LaFarge's spiritual source lay in art reaching back to the twelfth century where, said Henry Adams, he "not only felt at home, but felt a sort of ownership." Each of his creations, whether the watercolor of a single waterlily or a Biblical scene, was born into a religiously maintained world of art where it could live the double life of the thing seen and the truth remembered, remembered by virtue of past and sometimes exotic art. It was a celebration of the imagination, if imagination can mean art sustained in the mind. The "reverie" of Washington Allston would now seem to have been transformed into "memory."

Another artist who, beginning in the 1870s, turned more and more to a nostalgic art deeply imbedded in literature of the soul was Elihu Vedder. Hardly an ascetic, he nonetheless came to see his role as that of a seer creating moving works of that ". . . sad poetry which is the mark of the artist's temperament." Although his small well-observed landscapes have the frank, patterned charm of paintings by his Italian colleagues, his serious pictures entwine nature in artistic rhythms that derive their liveness from persuasive linear form rather than any suggestion of verisimilitude. Art, not nature, provides the suggestion of special meaning. "Faith" and "Doubt" when they surround the sorrowing "Soul" are personified as a fifteenth-century angel seen in the manner of Burne-Jones and a coldly styled head of a classical philosopher. Art, with its timeless historical flavor, could sublimate problems to a general realm of moral rumination. The rumination seems rarely to provide an answer, however; there is a continual questioning and a resigned sadness in this artistic world.

Vedder was, in his way, a survivor of an earlier Italianate group of Americans, but a similar nostalgia, if not a similar style, also pervades many of the works of painters like Abbott Thayer and George de Forest Brush. Thayer's well-bred virgins breathe an air made pure by art, not nature. Their familiar faces are transported to a different realm by Renaissance draperies and the mellow tones of aging masterpieces. It was an atmosphere in which symbol can dwell; it is hard to know whether to call a painting a mother and child, the Virgin and Child, or a personification of motherhood or charity. In a way it is all three at the same time, and as many more associations are welcome as the memory cares to furnish.

Although some have thought it strange that a fashionable

portrait painter should turn to allegorical mural painting, John Singer Sargent's preoccupation in his later years is not so surprising if one considers the position of art and the artist at the end of the century. In his Boston Public Library murals he approached religion and philosophy through the special language of art that allowed him to converse directly with different cultures. To repeat the visual formulation of a past concept was to show sympathy for, if not complete understanding of, the idea itself, and an assemblage of images could be the unification in one mind of many diverse creeds. His *Triumph of Religion* is, in its way, also a summa of the arts; it is almost impossible to separate the two. And it is the artist who leads the philosopher and the theologian into this understanding. The murals are not philosophical illustrations in any usual sense. The master of painting, even portrait painting, had potentially a mastery over the whole realm of the spirit.

The art of personal introspection well steeped in past cultures appears very differently in the hands of a peculiar genius like Albert Pinkham Ryder, yet his richly allusive paintings are also dependent for their understanding on a willing and well-stocked mind. Although highly personal, they also exist in the world of ancient balladry, the Bible and the Forest of Arden. But memory for Ryder strikes well beyond the schools; his haunting forms convoke what Jung would call a racial memory, an underlying common denominator arrived at not through Sargent's compilations but through Blakian insight. Jonah, observed by a benign Jehovah, embodies all our hopes and shadowy fears as he flounders in the massive waves. Mary Magdalene meets Christ in a quivering, dematerializing atmosphere and crouches in a gesture that recalls Giotto, Titian and the long tradition in art. And yet the moment is profoundly personal. It is as if the whole of the past lives in the intensity of the immediate artistic experience.

Some would maintain that these historically conscious aesthetic tendencies were not religious but, on the contrary, simply substituted the artistic for the religious experience. In some cases that may be so. But the matter seems more an equivocation of terms than a dispute over content. The part that the new aesthetic consciousness was to play in some early twentieth-century religious movements would suggest that this may have been just the first stage in the redefinition of religiosity itself, a process destined to continue.

Catalogue to the Exhibition

Jane Dillenberger

Introduction

This catalogue and the exhibition it documents represent the first large-scale showing of art expressing the religious impulse as it was experienced by American artists during the period of the eighteenth and nineteenth centuries. It is unusual also in juxtaposing the work of academically trained artists, referred to on occasion as "high art," with the work of the traditional, so-called "naive" artists. Not until the 1930s was the work of naive artists recognized by a group of perceptive collectors and museum directors as possessing a particular vision and excellence. Now naive art (which has also been referred to as "primitive" or "folk" art) has its own scholars, connoisseurs, collectors and museums, but for the most part it has been exhibited separately. In this exhibition such works are intermingled with those by academic artists since they often share the same impulse or subject matter, and it is illuminating to compare and contrast the ways in which similar material has been envisioned by artists of widely differing backgrounds.

In the process of preparing the exhibition, some seven hundred works relating to religious ideas were studied, providing a rather comprehensive view of the religious impulse in American art. The exhibition must be viewed, then, as only a sample drawn from a considerably larger body; quite different emphases might have been possible. There is no simple view of this complex subject.

Locating the works of art was a fascinating but time-consuming task. Many were almost literally unearthed from the subterranean keeps of museums, unexhibited for so long that decades of accumulated dust enshrouded them. Each discovery led to further possibilities: neither the exhibition nor the documentation of the works of art included can be considered as definitive. But it is a substantial beginning.

Until recently, historians of American art have tended to consider as peripheral paintings deriving from the religious impulse by major artists. (Barbara Novak's impressive book, *American Painting in the Nineteenth Century,* is a recent exception.) Furthermore, museums are much less likely to exhibit these works or call attention to their particular character. Yet for the artists themselves the religious content was by no means negligible.

Not unexpectedly, the art in the exhibition represents the predominantly Protestant nature of American culture during this period. The Southwest panel paintings and carvings are an obvious exception, created by and for a particular Roman Catholic community. Other than this, art for emerging American Catholicism was largely imported and sometimes consisted of copies of major works, most of uneven quality. Generally speaking, there is no figurative religious art relating to the Jewish community, but Moses Ezekiel's sculpture and stained glass designs form an interesting group which are an exception, and come from the latter part of the nineteenth century. The American Indians and that surviving from African sources belong to a different study.

It is perhaps surprising that the art does not always reflect trends in the literary domain. American intellectual life of the period was much concerned with the "American Adam." But the mythic Adam of American literature discussed by R. W. B. Lewis in his *The American Dream* (Chicago, 1955), or by David W. Noble in his *The Eternal Adam and the New World Garden* (New York, 1968) is hardly to be found as direct expression in American art of this period. A major sculpture of Adam and Eve, and several paintings, do exist, and are included in this exhibition, but the role of Adam in art is quite different from his role in the literature of the nineteenth century.

The analysis of the subject matter which follows must be viewed as providing signposts on terrain not yet fully charted. Joshua Taylor has provided a significant interpretive essay on American art in the context of literary and religious currents. Mine is the more limited task of commenting on the subject matter of the works themselves, and the ways in which traditional, inherited iconography has at times been transformed by both academically trained and naive artists in the American scene.

Some Reflections on Biblical Imagery in American Art

The image of God, the acts of creation, the lives of the patriarchs, the persons of the prophets, events in Israel's history, the image of Jesus, New Testament episodes, the lives of the saints and their martyrdoms, even the doctrines and dogma of the church—these have been formed and transformed by artists of the past. Academically-oriented American artists, from the time of Benjamin West and John Singleton Copley, went to

England and the Continent, and there confronted monuments of the past. What they saw and how they saw can be reconstructed from their letters and conversations. Certain of these materials are published here in connection with particular works of art. Something of these artists' encounters with the art of the past can be deduced from an examination of their own works of art. Washington Allston's *Jeremiah* (ill. p.65), while original in composition and conception, shows its indebtedness to Michelangelo's *Moses*; Rimmer's drawing of *God Creating the Sun and Moon* (ill. p.27) is inextricably linked to Michelangelo's *God* of the Sistine Chapel. However, for the artists who remained outside of the academic tradition, this heritage of imagery was received and transmitted through illustrated Bibles, engravings and woodcuts from English and Continental sources. By the late eighteenth century, illustrated Bibles were published in such places as Worcester, Massachusetts, and Philadelphia, and New York. The transmission of imagery was sometimes complex, as in the watercolor of *The Baptisam of Our Savour* (ill. p.99) by Ann Johnson which is clearly copied after the lithograph (ill. p.101) of John Baker, who in turn undoubtedly based his upon the reproduction of an earlier English or Continental painting.

The Image of God

Although the image of God is very rarely seen in American art, two quite different representations are each fascinating in their own ways; Ryder's God in the painting of *Jonah* (ill. p.26) and Rimmer's drawing of *God Creating the Sun and Moon*.

In Ryder's painting, Jonah is the subject, but it is God who engages our attention. Contrary to ancient tradition it is the left hand of God which is raised in blessing; his right hand grasps a dark globe with a dynamism that has more in common with the effort of a bowler than with the traditional still and easy balance characteristic of the Almighty who holds the orb as a symbol of rulership over the earth. Only the head and hands of the Lord emerge from the low, scudding clouds, as he seems to thrust forward in space, his eyes glancing intently sidelong, apparently watching the great fish he has appointed to swallow up Jonah.

If the Book of Jonah is read with Ryder's painting in view, it is clear that the artist is not depicting the drama of Jonah's flight nor his shipboard experience, nor the subsequent episode when Jonah is thrown into the sea, for when this was done "the sea ceased from its raging." Rather, Ryder depicts Jonah's experience of God when he prayed to the Lord from the belly of the fish. Here the Lord, answering his prophet Jonah, enters into the drama of flight, descends into Sheol, and is an active protagonist in salvation. The Lord is not an all-seeing, all-knowing overseer whose presence guarantees the right outcome. Ryder represents him as a force, as much psychic as physical, enlisted on the side of the prophet. This internalized appropriation and rendering of God is a marked transformation of the tradition. Michelangelo's God works by fiat and even Blake's early nineteenth-century version, for all its similarities to Ryder, unlike Ryder represents a God in whom good and evil are conjoined.

Rimmer's powerful drawing of *God Creating the Sun and Moon* is clearly related to Michelangelo's fresco of the same subject. But the muscular, immense torso drawn by Rimmer has the energy and vitality of a Paul Bunyan rather than the pervasive power of the classically-inspired God of Michelangelo.

Old Testament Imagery

The mighty acts of creation, except for the single drawing by Rimmer, are not found in American art of the period 1700–1900. Adam and Eve are often represented in the Garden, usually surrounded by an opulent natural setting, as if the Garden had just been created, and the event of the Fall is yet to come. Field's *Garden of Eden* (ill. p.115) and the watercolor by an unknown artist (ill. p.97) seem to bear analogy to the many references in nineteenth-century literature to America as the New World Garden. However, while the literature focuses to a remarkable degree on Adam, there are few parallels in the art of the period. We see in Crawford's sculpture, *Adam and Eve* (ill. p.77), a regretful Adam who should belong to Emerson's "party of memory," rather than the "party of hope," but the sense of the epic, or mythic is missing in this tidy, adolescent Adam with his neat coiffure and bathing-trunks symmetrically embossed with overlapping fig-leaves.

But if Adam does not appear alone, Eve does, in sculpture. *Eve Tempted* (ill. p.17) and *Eve Disconsolate* provided Hiram Powers with the possibility of making a nude figure acceptable to a prudish public by a title suggesting an allusive morality. The

Albert Pinkham Ryder (1847–1917). *Jonah* (detail). (ca. 1890).
Oil on canvas. 26½ x 33½". National Collection of Fine Arts, Smithsonian Institution, Washington, D.C.: Gift of John Gellatly. [Not in
exhibition].

90. William Rimmer. *God the Father Creating the Sun and Moon.* 1869.
Sanguine over pencil on paper. 17¾ x 12¾". Fogg Art Museum, Harvard University, Cambridge, Massachusetts: Louise E. Bettens Fund.

flesh of these American Eves has a kind of innocence, whether Eve is depicted before or after the Fall. Hawthorne, after visiting Powers' studio in Florence, remarked that the whiteness of the marble removed the figure "into a sort of spiritual region, and so gave chaste permission to those nudities which would otherwise suggest immodesty." Powers' Eve has a specificity of form and a sense of inwardness that remove her from the realm of classical myth and sensual association.

That Powers' Eve after the Fall is designated as *Eve Disconsolate* is significant. The loss of Eden and the putting on of mortality demand more than dejection, gloominess, and melancholy.

Although Adam and Eve are found in few examples, the serpent can be said to do better. Sinuous and sensuous, the serpent appears in many forms in scenes of the Garden of Eden, on statues of Eve, in C. W. Peale's painting of *Noah;* in Greenough's pair of statues of *Christ* and *Lucifer* (ill. pp.73,75) where a phallic-looking serpent coils about the base of each. Much later it appears in John Singer Sargent's bronze *Crucifix* (ill. pp.179, 181). In the latter, Christ is seen on the cross between the crouching figures of Adam and Eve, and the serpent is entwined about the feet of the Christ, its head pierced by the same nail which fixes Christ's feet to the cross.

Abel, too, is represented with surprising frequency. Thomas Cole's *The Dead Abel* (ill. p.107) with Abel lying supine in the foreground and Cain retreating in the distance, is one of many known examples by a professional artist. Mrs. H. Weed's embroidery, from the hand of a naive artist, *Adam and Eve Mourning over the Dead Abel* (ill. p.95) presents the scene with rhetorical gestures. William Rimmer and Elihu Vedder painted this episode and Greenough did a plaster of Abel while in Rome.

These may all be related to Salomon Gessner's book, *The Dead Abel,* a bathetic eighteenth-century German elaboration of the Biblical event, which was translated into English and widely read. By 1762 a third English edition was published in London. William Blake did a drawing of the subject of Abel and Byron wrote a poem on it. Indeed, this preoccupation with the Biblical episode may indicate not only the theme of human sin and the sons of Cain as the inheritors of bestiality but also a general fascination with the theme of fratricide during the eighteenth and nineteenth centuries.

Moses appears a larger-than-life figure in two important commissioned cycles of paintings, one at the end of the eighteenth century, the other at the end of the nineteenth century. The first is Benjamin West's series of paintings for King George III's chapel which was projected for Windsor but never built. The Moses cycle is now in the Memorial Chapel of Bob Jones University. The second is in John Singer Sargent's frieze of the Prophets for the Boston Public Library, in which Moses is the central figure. Moses was the subject of a major large work by William Page for which drawings still exist.

But more often, in both high and naive art, Moses is pictured as the infant foundling, discovered by Pharaoh's daughter at the river's brink, an event requiring a landscape setting. Painters like Frederick Church depicted it as occurring in an exotic, panoramic landscape, so vast that the figures of Moses and his rescuers are insignificant.

In Erastus Salisbury Field's series on the Plagues of Egypt, Moses is conspicuous by his absence. He is seen in only one of the series, a small figure standing on the steps at the right with Aaron who is holding his rod at his side. Field prefers to concentrate on the events which resulted from Moses' conversations with the Lord. A careful examination of the *Israelites Crossing the Red Sea* (ill. p.119) shows several large ghostly figures, pentimenti, behind the phalanx of oncoming cattle. One of these was no doubt intended to represent Moses.

In the art of the past Moses is depicted in heroic dimensions as the deliverer from bondage, or as the law giver, or at the moment of his theophany at the burning bush. These themes, so often represented in European art, do not occur in the American religious art in this study.

In the material surveyed, Abraham appears only in a drawing by Copley of Abraham and Isaac. However, Abraham's concubine, Hagar, and their son Ishmael were often represented in late eighteenth- and nineteenth-century art both in Europe and America. This story also provides the occasion for a landscape setting, but its popularity in this country may stem from its essential theme, that of going out into the wilderness with the assurance that the Lord will make a nation of Ishmael. The theme of founding a new nation under God, which runs through political speeches, documents, sermonic interpolations, and public utterances, suggests that Americans read Biblical stories in the light of their own experience.

Similarly, Lot fleeing Sodom with the guidance of angels, and Noah's going forth in the Ark, can be seen as parables of deliverance through divine guidance, that the chosen of God might survive and live in a new land. Both of these subjects occur with considerable frequency in American art of the nineteenth century.

The Image of Christ

Horatio Greenough remarked that "the prejudice, or rather the conviction of the Protestant mind has deterred many from a representation of our Saviour." He differed from his mentor Allston, who, frustrated by his failure to represent Christ in a painting, declared that all painters, ancient and modern, also had failed "to give even a tolerable idea of the Saviour." Allston foreswore ever attempting it again, adding, "Besides I think his character too holy and sacred to be attempted by the pencil." Greenough disagreed, believing that Christ was a legitimate subject for art, and such paintings and sculptures should be accepted, like the hymns and prayers of the pious, "as fervent aspirations after the good and beautiful." Greenough's argument for the recreation of the Christ image draws religious, moral and aesthetic categories into a single conception.

Greenough followed his own precepts, for he did two marble busts of Christ. Both of these are influenced by the Renaissance Christ type which he encountered in works such as Michelangelo's early *Pietá* and Leonardo's Christ of the *Last Supper*. This idealized, classicized image can be traced to the Apollonic Christ of the early Christian era, and before that to classical Apollo types. This Christ is serene in suffering and rules over heaven and earth even from the cross. It was this image of Christ-Apollo that William Page recreated to suit his Swedenborgian speculations, and that Hiram Powers preferred.

Another type of Christ draws mankind to him, not by his transcendence, but through his suffering. In this exhibition this type is represented by Henry Ossawa Tanner's *The Savior* and Moses Ezekiel's *Ecce Homo* (ill. p.175). There are other examples too, notably the Christ images of New Mexico. That Tanner's and Ezekiel's Christ images are by artists who were from an ethnic minority in their own day, as they would be now, is to be noted. Tanner's Negro and Indian blood was the reason for his living abroad as an expatriate, even after he had attained a fame never accorded his teacher, Thomas Eakins, during his lifetime. Moses Ezekiel, a Jewish sculptor, received honors and prizes from Continental sources before he was recognized in his homeland. The type of Christ depicted by Tanner and Ezekiel is characterized by a narrow, worn face, large dark eyes, long hair and dark moustache and beard.

New Testament Subject Matter

As for New Testament subjects in American art of the period, considerable emphasis falls upon the teachings of Jesus—the parables of the Prodigal Son, the Good Samaritan and the Good Shepherd. This is abundantly true in naive art, though each of the above subjects was treated also by academic artists.

Post-Resurrection subject matter also appears; Jesus' appearance to the Magdalene, painted more than once by Ryder, and by anonymous naive artists; Jesus' appearances to the Apostles when Thomas asked to see His wounds occurs both in Haidt's work and in John Landis' *Jesus in the Upper Room* (ill. p.103); Christ on the Road to Emmaus occurs in several of the eighteenth-century Albany paintings. The Ascension of Christ was depicted by Copley and West, and by John LaFarge at the end of the century in his famous mural for the Church of the Ascension in New York.

Thus the occurrence of didactic themes, and themes related to Jesus' appearances after the Resurrection, are to be noted as characteristic for both high art and naive art.

New Testament events which are not depicted, or depicted rarely, are of interest since they evidently indicate themes in which the artists and their patrons were not interested. The Nativity as such, and the Adoration of the Shepherds, is replaced by the Adoration of the Magi. The Baptism of Christ is a subject infrequently found, as is the Last Supper. (The latter was painted however by Erastus Salisbury Field, and was based on Leonardo's famous painting which the untraveled Field must have known through a print.) The Resurrection is most often represented either by the Marys at the tomb (a strange painting by John Quidor, and several examples in naive art), or the *Two Disciples at the Tomb* (ill. p.161) by Tanner, or the Easter morning encounter of the Magdalene with the risen Christ. Paintings of certain great festivals of the Church, such as Pentecost and the Transfiguration, do not appear in this exhibition.

Related Subjects

The saints, of course, are not represented in this art that derived from the Protestant ethos. But the image of the Guardian Angel occurs often. In this exhibition there is an oil sketch by Thomas Cole (ill.p.113) for the Angel who guides man from infancy through the perils of life to eternity in his series of paintings, entitled the *Voyage of Life*. Cole painted several sets of the four series that comprised the *Voyage of Life*, and he had them reproduced in sets of engravings as well. Cole's *Guardian Angel* seems a comfortable companion—a familiar, domesticated guide rather than the exalted messenger of the Almighty.

There are references to the Guardian Angel in American poetry and Oliver Wendell Holmes wrote a novel with that title. The image itself derives from the story of Tobias in the Apocrypha. An angel instructed Tobias that he could cure the blindness of his father Tobit, by catching a fish, burning it, and anointing Tobit's eyes with the ashes. The angel became identified with the Archangel Raphael. It is in this guise that he is seen in the art of the Southwest, where Raphael always has a fish in hand as his attribute. The intimacy and charm of these panel paintings and carvings of the Archangel have their own verity, and need no comment.

The Guardian Angel as seen in Cole's paintings and in popular art apparently served a function in Protestant culture analagous to that of the saints for the Catholics of the Southwest.

Naive Art

The designation of "naive" for the work of artists who had no academic training or interest in academic values is admittedly awkward, and Grace Glueck's suggestion that the word "innocent" be used instead does not relieve one from the dilemma of using a term for a variety of works of art which have little in common except what they are not. Unlike naive artists, painters such as Copley, West, Allston, Cole, Page, Vedder, as well as the sculptors Greenough, Powers and Crawford, were not only trained in their craft, but studied the art of the preceding centuries as well as classical art; they consciously became the heirs of a long history of particular ways of seeing in the Western world. They were scions of the art of the past, becoming part of it and augmenting it with new growth. Thus, despite the variety in high art, it has a coherence that may be distinguished

as a line of development (if this term is not taken to mean betterment), and a cohesiveness. The naive artist, however, chooses the particular motifs from the artistic tradition which he wishes to adapt, and uses them to serve his personal vision.

A variety of talents and personal visions are evident in the naive art in this exhibition. Foremost among individual naive artists is Edward Hicks, the Quaker artist who, it is estimated, painted some eighty paintings of the Peaceable Kingdom, and Erastus Salisbury Field, the Massachusetts painter of the *Garden of Eden*, the Plagues of Egypt series, and the *Monument to the American Republic* (ill. p.121). Both of these artists could be described as folk artists—that is, both lived with and painted for a rural population, and both were essentially self-taught. Like the other naive artists, they derived motifs or settings from prints or Biblical illustrations. But these are radically transformed.

When one compares Benjamin West's painting of *William Penn's Treaty* with Hicks' appropriation of his composition as an episode in the background of the *Peaceable Kingdom*, one concludes that knowing the source is interesting, but that Hicks' transmutation makes the knowledge almost irrelevant. Similarly the various sources for Field's paintings are assimilated by him in various degrees, but his own idiom, his own vision, prevails throughout.

A group of religious carvings and paintings from the Southwest have a stylistic and iconographic identity that make them a group apart. Their creators, the santeros of what is now New Mexico, carried on the imagery of European Renaissance and Baroque art, painting and carving the many advocations of the Virgin, the Archangels Michael and Raphael, the Trinity, and the saints in forms that have a long history in European art. But in New Mexican naive art the grandiloquent, hieratic, and remote images of the Renaissance and Baroque become intimate, domesticated, and charming, like the St. Michael standing akimbo upon the *Dragon of Evil* (ill. p.125). New iconographic images appear in this isolated area, such as the *Good Shepherdess*, a feminine counterpart to the historic Good Shepherd image.

The naive designation is also to be applied to the work of students in young women's seminaries of the period. Part of their instruction in genteel accomplishments included drawing,

103. Henry Ossawa Tanner. *The Saviour.* (n.d.). Oil on plywood. 29⅛ x 21⅞". Museum of African Art / Frederick Douglass Institute, Washington, D.C.

needlework, and music. Betsy Lathrop's watercolor of *Japhthah's Return* (ill. p.83) is a notable example of this kind of art. Such drawings and paintings also draw upon sources in prints, illustrated books and Bibles. But again their sources are combined freely with data from their own observations to create a new work of art. Many of these artists are known to us through only one or two examples, and knowing their names or identifying their sources does not add significantly to our appreciation or knowledge of them. They are singular in the sense that they do indeed stand alone.

Naive and popular art must be distinguished. Popular art consists of illustrations made for the interests and sentiments of a mass audience, such as those appearing in *Harper's Weekly*, in Currier & Ives prints, and Thomas Nast's work. One such print, the lithograph of John Baker of the *Baptism of Our Saviour* is shown in this exhibition since it is the source of one of the naive artist's paintings. Some of this work has technical expertise, and a topical pungency, but it does not convey the personal vision which the naive artist puts before us with a singular directness, innocence of eye, and fervor of spirit.

Plates

An exhibition of this scope could be organized in many ways; as, e.g., by strict chronology, subject matter, or related schools. It seemed better and more instructive, however, to organize the materials for this catalogue into groups based on a general similarity of intent on the part of the artists, and to order the groups on the basis of rough chronology.

Group I, p. 34, catalogue numbers 1 through 7, consists of eighteenth-century Biblical paintings, which are only remotely related to the academic tradition in painting (unknown artists, John Valentine Haidt).

Group II, p. 46, catalogue numbers 8 through 29, follows the academic tradition through a variety of changes into the third quarter of the nineteenth century (Samuel King, John Singleton Copley, Benjamin West, Joshua Shaw, Washington Allston, William Sidney Mount, Rembrandt Peale, Horatio Greenough, Thomas Crawford, William Page, Daniel Huntington).

Group III, p. 81, catalogue numbers 30 through 60, the largest section, comprises works that closely follow the dictates of religious teaching, largely sectarian (unknown artists, Betsy B. Lathrop, Mary Ann Willson, Charles Peale, Edward Hicks, Mrs. H. Weed, Ann Johnson, John Baker, John Landis, Thomas Cole, Erastus Salisbury Field, Carl Christian Anton Christensen).

Group IV, p. 123, catalogue numbers 61 through 86, provides two rich traditions unrelated to the mainstream of American art, the Spanish tradition of the southwest, and works from the German Pennsylvania community (unknown artists, José Aragón, Pedro Fresquis, Juan Ramon Velasquez, Rafael Aragón, Jose Benito Ortega, The Reverend George Geistweite).

Group V, p. 141, catalogue numbers 87 through 108, presents a range of independent artists of the second half of the nineteenth century (Artist Unknown, William Rimmer, George Inness, Edwin Romanzo Elmer, Robert Loftin Newman, Albert Pinkham Ryder, Thomas Eakins, Henry Ossawa Tanner).

Group VI, p. 163, catalogue numbers 109 through 123, consists of a few examples of a phenomenon of the late nineteenth century in which the aesthetic mode and religious feeling at times became synonymous (John LaFarge, Elihu Vedder, Moses J. Ezekiel, Abbott H. Thayer, John Singer Sargent, Tiffany Studios).

To aid in the use of the catalogue, an alphabetical list of artists and an index of titles are provided at the end of this catalogue, on page 186.

Dimensions are in inches, height preceding width preceding depth, except where otherwise noted. Dates enclosed in parentheses do not appear on works. Illustrated works are indicated with an asterisk. Except as noted in individual entries, all works are included in all showings of the exhibition.

Certain key works are missing from the exhibition because of their immense size or fragile condition, or their permanence of installation. Noted below are a group of such paintings and their respective locations:

> Benjamin West, Paintings for Windsor Chapel commissioned by King George III. Memorial Chapel, Bob Jones University, Greenville, South Carolina.
>
> Washington Allston, "The Dead Man Revived by Touching the Bones of the Prophet Elisha." The Pennsylvania Academy of Fine Arts, Philadelphia.
>
> Washington Allston, "Belshazzar's Feast." The Detroit Institute of Arts.
>
> Thomas Eakins, "The Crucifixion." Philadelphia Museum of Art.
>
> John LaFarge, "The Ascension." Church of the Ascension, New York.
>
> John LaFarge, Decoration of Trinity Church, Boston.
>
> John Singer Sargent, "The History of Judaism and Christianity." The Boston Public Library.

*1. Artist Unknown. *Four Evangelists Writing the Gospels.* (ca. 1700–1725). Oil on panel. 29¼ x 35⅞". Albany Institute of History and Art, Albany, New York.

This painting belongs to a group with religious subject matter done by several artists working in Albany County, New York, in the early eighteenth century. The Albany Institute of History and Art owns the largest group of these paintings. Illustrated Dutch Bibles printed in Amsterdam and Dordrecht in 1702 are sources for some of them.

Despite the classical architectural setting (freely rendered with amusing disjunctions of perspective), and the spectral light, presumably offering divine illumination, the figures give the impression of concentrating upon a domestic or business reckoning. A sturdy angel holds a tablet within range of St. Matthew's nearsighted eyes. St. Mark frowns at his labor, while his lion peers from beneath the table-cover with such individuality of feature and expression that he seems more human than the Apostles. St. John looks toward the light of inspiration, while St. Luke writes doggedly on.

The animals accompanying the Evangelists have a long symbolic history in ecclesiastical art. They originate with the passages describing Ezekiel's vision "out of the mist thereof came the likeness of four living creatures...as for the likeness of their faces, they four had the face of a man, and the face of a lion...the face of an ox...the face of an eagle." From the fifth century A.D., these beasts have symbolized the Evangelists in art.

While the architectural setting posed problems, the artist rendered familiar objects such as the inkwell, with its one quill pen, with the faithfulness of observation of homely detail frequently found in the work of untrained or naive artists.
Reference: "Hudson Valley Paintings, 1700–1750, in the Albany Institute of History and Art," 1959.

*2. Artist Unknown. *Adoration of the Magi.* (ca. 1700–1725). Oil on canvas. 29½ x 36⅝". Abby Aldrich Rockefeller Folk Art Collection, Williamsburg, Virginia.

The artist describes the Adoration leaving nothing undefined. He obviously delights in the pattern of the spears against the sky, the helmets of the Magi's attendants, their garments and shields. On the ground is the kneeling Magus's sceptre and crowned hat, the latter so flattened in form that it is best identified through comparison with Benjamin West's Magi.

Noteworthy in this painting, as in West's, is the survival of a tradition originating in northern Europe—that one of the Magi was a black, signifying that Christ came to all races of mankind.

The *Adoration of the Magi* appears to be related to the group of religious paintings now owned by the Albany Institute of History and Art. Like other Albany paintings, it is probably based on Biblical illustrations.

*3. Artist Unknown. *The Finding of Moses.* (ca. 1700–1725). Oil on canvas. 27 x 35". Abby Aldrich Rockefeller Folk Art Collection, Williamsburg, Virginia.

The artist has clearly indicated the reeds where the infant Moses' basket is discovered. Behind Pharaoh's daughter, one of three attendants offers her breast, having been instructed to take the child and nurse it; the artist's adaptation of the Biblical material is patently free.

Buildings and what appears to be a bridge occupy the middle distance, but the arches for the bridge support nothing. The vigorous dark and light pattern shows the artist's sensitivity to the design of the whole, as well as his talent for lively narrative.

The great archetypal figure of Moses as conceived by Michelangelo, and the Moses of Rembrandt holding the tablets of the Law, are both remote from the Moses depicted by American artists. In American art, Moses is often the infant, a changeling, the object of discovery, evoking emotions of tenderness and protectiveness, rather than fear and awe.

John Valentine Haidt (1700–1780)

John Valentine Haidt was born in Germany and began his artistic career when forty-five or forty-six years of age in the Moravian community of Herrnhaag. His father, a goldsmith, taught him this trade, though the boy wanted to become a minister. However, he studied drawing for three years at the Royal Academy of Arts in Berlin. Later, when established in London as a goldsmith, he joined the Moravians after a profound religious experience at a Moravian love feast in London. He became a lay preacher in England, then returned to Germany in 1746.

His motivation for devoting himself entirely to painting came when the Moravian church was going through the so-called Sifting Period. Haidt, who was impressed by the Moravian emphasis on the blood and wounds of the Saviour, felt that the Moravians were straying from the true gospel. Thus, he wrote Count Zinzendorf and asked to be allowed to paint rather than preach, saying, "For, I thought, if they will not preach the martyrdom of God anymore, I will paint it all the more vigorously." Permission was granted and Count Zinzendorf, who had already asked him to do one painting, increased the request to nine. In 1754 he left England with his family for Bethlehem, Pennsylvania, then the center of the Moravian church in this country. In the communal economic system of the Moravians there was no such thing as a non-religious occupation. The church supported him, even providing him with a painting room. As official church painter, he did not have to get commissions from congregations or individuals. He painted portraits as well as many Biblical scenes, and indeed was very productive. He concluded his memoir in 1767 with the words, "I hardly need to mention that I have painted, because almost all the congregations have some of my work, which the dear Savior has also let be a blessing to many a heart."

Haidt's paintings were intended, as Walter Peters writes, "literally as visual aids in expounding the Scriptures not only in Moravian churches but also in Moravian mission chapels among the Indian nations and other mission fields." Though Haidt did portraits, a large group of the extant paintings are preponderantly on Passion subjects; there are several versions of the Crucifixion, Christ in Gethsemane, the Ecce Homo, and Lamentation over the Dead Christ. All of these emphasize the blood and sweat and anguish of Christ, recalling the "incomparable hymn" by Count Zinzendorf which moved Haidt at the time of his conversion: "The Savior's blood and righteousness / Our beauty is, our glorious dress; / Thus well arrayed we need not fear, / When in His presence we appear."

Today many of Haidt's paintings are on view at the Moravian Historical Society in Nazareth, Pennsylvania, and at the Archives of the Moravian Church in Bethlehem, Pennsylvania. *Reference:* (1) Vernon Nelson, "John Valentine Haidt," exhibition catalogue, Abby Aldrich Rockefeller Folk Art Collection, Williamsburg, Virginia, 1966; (2) Walter L. Peters, "The Religious Paintings of Johann Valentin Haidt," in *The Moravian,* vol. 109, no. 1, January 1964.

4. John Valentine Haidt. *The Crucifixion.* (1757). Oil on canvas. 40½ x 51″. The Moravian Historical Society, Nazareth, Pennsylvania.

The most important American painting of the Crucifixion is Thomas Eakins' stark, solitary figure of Christ set against a bleak landscape. The representation of the Crucifixion as an historical-ideal event (as Anna Jameson terms it), though common in European and Renaissance and Baroque art in Italy and in the north, is most uncommon in American art. Haidt must have seen many European Crucifixion paintings during his residence and travels abroad; his own work is filled with recollections and borrowings from European art.

When Haidt painted the Passion themes in Bethlehem, Pennsylvania, he followed European prototypes, showing the full complement of *personae* so seldom found in American depictions of the Crucifixion. Haidt has chosen here to portray the moment in which Jesus' side is pierced as being simultaneous with the breaking of the legs of the unrepentant thief. As in his other paintings, strange differences in the scale of the figures make the spatial pattern arbitrary. The helmeted figure, left foreground, is immense in contrast to the woman with crossed arms who gazes upward. Despite these awkwardnesses and Haidt's unassimilated appropriations from European art, he succeeds in communicating his personal piety.

5. John Valentine Haidt. *Christ Revealing His Wound (with Thomas).* (1757). Oil on canvas. 51 x 40½″. The Moravian Historical Society, Nazareth, Pennsylvania.

This is an unusual depiction of the post-Resurrection Biblical episode of the doubting Thomas who is told by Christ to place a hand in His side. Haidt's Christ guides the hand of the dazed Thomas literally into the wound, which is again shown on the left side.

Diaries of the period, as well as Count Zinzendorf's hymns, reveal the Moravian emphasis upon the blood and wounds of Christ at this period. In the "Bethlehem Diary," Vol. I, 1742–1744, many references to the wounds of Christ appear; for example, in telling of a Baptism the writer goes on to relate:

> Then there was sung "The bloody Sweat which such Heat did from Thee flow," etc., during which Bro. Ludwig (Count Zinzendorf) imparted absolution to her as he imposed his hands upon her; then he baptized her "with the Water & Blood from the Heart and Side of Jesus, in the Name of the Father, the Son, & the Holy Ghost...."

*6. John Valentine Haidt. *Lamentation over Christ's Body.* (ca. 1760). Oil on canvas. 25 x 30″. The Moravian Historical Society, Nazareth, Pennsylvania.

The emphasis on the Saviour's blood and wounds is reflected in Moravian hymns as well as in Haidt's paintings: "Thy blood so dear and precious, / Love made Thee shed for me; / Oh, may I now, dear Jesus, / Love Thee most fervently" (Moravian Hymnal No. 498).

In this painting, the wounded body of Christ is given maximum exposure. The wound in Christ's side is traditionally portrayed on the right side of his torso, whereas Haidt consistently placed it on the left. The only exception I know of is a small Haidt drawing that clearly derives from a Bellini painting, in the Bethlehem Archives.

The weeping Magdalene in the foreground is enormous in contrast to Mary, who supports Christ's arm. These strange disjunctions of space and size combine with the insistent crescent of the massive body of Christ, lending expressive power to the painting.

This painting came from the Moravian Brethren's House in Nazareth, Pennsylvania, which became active in 1758. Thus it is assumed that Haidt's painting must be only slightly after that date.

*7. John Valentine Haidt. *Christ Before Herod.* (ca. 1765). Oil on canvas. 24½ x 29½". The Moravian Historical Society, Nazareth, Pennsylvania.

As in Haidt's other paintings, odd inconsistencies of scale distort into enormity the chief priest, left foreground, and the great dog, right foreground. By contrast, the figure of Queen Herodias is tiny. Herod and Herodias, in gleaming eighteenth-century costume, might be models of contemporary Continental rulers. Despite the richness of detail, the figure of Christ explicitly dominates the scene, an effect Haidt achieved by central placement, the white garments, and the quietude of Christ's mien and posture contrasted with the gesticulating crowd.

This painting, dating from about 1765, originally belonged to the Moravian Settlement in Hope, New Jersey. Contemporary diaries reveal that the emphasis on Christ's blood and wounds was not then so intense as formerly.

*8. Samuel King. *Portrait of Ezra Stiles.* 1771. Oil on canvas. 33½ x 27½". Yale University Art Gallery, New Haven, Connecticut: Bequest of Dr. Charles C. Foote.

The Reverend Ezra Stiles was one of the most learned men of his time. He was a tutor at Yale College, studied and practiced law, accepted a call to the ministry of the Second Congregational Church in Newport, and in 1778 became President of Yale College, remaining in that post until his death in 1795. This portrait of him, at 43 years of age, is a fascinating document. Fortunately, Ezra Stiles wrote faithfully and extensively in his diary and his entry for August, 1771, provides a complete explanation of the curious symbols which appear in the painting and an explication of the books with their titles clearly visible on the shelf behind him:

> This day Mr. King finished my Picture. He began it last year—but went over the face again now, & added Emblems &c. The Piece is made up thus. The Effigies sitting in a Green Elbow Chair, in a Teaching Attitude, with the right hand on the Breast, and the Left holding a preaching Bible. Behind & on his left side is a part of a Library—two Shelves of Books—a Folio shelf with *Eusebij Hist. Ecc.,* Livy, Du Halde's Histy of China, and one inscribed Talmud B., Aben Ezra, Rabbi Selomoh Jarchi in hebrew Letters, and a little below R. Moses Ben Maimon Norch Nevochim...
>
> On the other Shelf are Newton's Principia, Plato, Watts, Doddridge, Cudworths Intellectual System; & also the New Engld primaeval Divines Hooker, Chauncy, Mather, Cotton.
>
> At my Right hand stands a Pillar. On the Shaft is one Circle and one Trajectory around a solar point, as an emblem of the Newtonian or Pythagorean System of the Sun & Plants & Comets... At the Top of the visible part of the Pillar & on the side of the Wall is an Emblem of the Universe or intellectual World. It is as it were one sheet of Omniscience. In a central Glory is the name [Hebrew letters for "God"] surrounded with white Spots on a Field of azure, from each Spot ascend three hair Lines denoting the Tendencies of Minds to Deity & Communion with the Trinity in the divine Light: These Spots denote *(Innocency,)* a Spirit, a World, Clusters of Systems of Worlds, & their

Tendencies to the eternal central yet universal omnipresent Light. This world is represented by a Cluster of Minds whose central Tendencies are turned off from God to Earth, self & created good—and also in a state of Redemption. Intervening is the Crucifixion of Christ between two Thieves—both Tendencies going off, but one turned back to the Light. Denotes also a converted & an unconverted Man.

> At a little Distance on the Left hand is a black Spot—the Receptacle of fallen Angels & the finally wicked... And the collection of moral Evil & Misery, in comparison with the moral Perfection & Happiness of the immense Universe, is but a small Spot... So that under this small minutesimal Exception of the Misery of all the fallen Angels & even most of the Posterity of Adam,... we may say ALL HAPPY IN GOD.
>
> These Emblems are more descriptive of my Mind, than the Effigies of my Face...

Reference: Bulletin of the Associates in Fine Arts at Yale University, Vol. 23, September, 1957, No. 3.

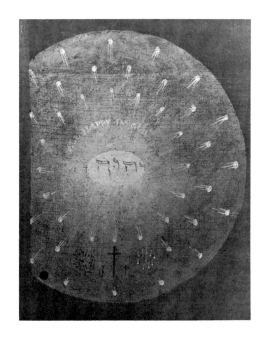

*9. John Singleton Copley. *The Ascension.* (1775). Oil on canvas. 32½ x 29½". Museum of Fine Arts, Boston: Bequest of Susan Greene Dexter.

John Singleton Copley achieved success and fame as a portraitist in America as well as in England where he permanently settled in 1755. Copley's religious-subject paintings, less well known than his portraits, form a varied and interesting group.

The Ascension, painted during Copley's first visit to Rome, was the first of this group. He wrote a long account to Henry Pelham, his step-brother, explaining his conception of the event. This letter is a remarkable document. Although we have other nineteenth-century artists' accounts and reflections on their subjects, these most often read like explanations after the fact. Copley instead writes with the fervor of one who has seized his subject imaginatively:

> I have always . . . considered the Assention as one of the most Sublime Subjects . . . I considered how the Appostles would be affected at that Instant, weither they would be scattered over the Ground inattentive to the Action . . . or weither they would croud together to hear the Charge to Peter, and when that was given weither they would not be asstonish'd at their Masters rising from the Earth and full of the Godhead Assend up into Heaven. no one who reads the Account in the first Chapter of the Acts can be at a moments loss to decide that they would be so asstonish'd, and after Crouding together to hear what Christ said to St. Peter with vast attention in their countinances, they would (keeping their places) and their attention to the Assending Christ Absorbed in holy Adoration, worship him as he rose from the Earth . . . no thought could at that Instant intrude it self into their minds, already fully possessed with Holy wonder. some may naturally be supposed to fall on their knees: others with hands uplifted standing worship him. Some would look steadfastly on him: others would bow their heads and in deep adoration with Eyes fixt on the Ground worship him with hands spread or on the breast but all inattentive to one another. but two Angels stood by them; and spake to them. this would naturally ingage those that were next to them, and as it were awaked from a trans, turn with surprise to hear what they said to them. it would be just to observe that the Appostolick Carracter forbids to make the expression of Asstonishment very great. it should be tempered with Love and contain Majesty of behaviour acquired by many times being spectators of the Power of Christ exercised in Miracle of a Stupendious nature. . . .

The letter continues at length telling of his studies of Raphael's paintings and of his technical procedure. Copley was pleased with the finished painting and remarked to his family in Boston that Piranesi and the artist Gavin Hamilton had both praised it. *Reference:* Guernsey Jones, *Letters and Papers of John Singleton Copley and Henry Pelham,* Boston, 1914. Volume LXXI of the Massachusetts Historical Society Collections.

Benjamin West (1738–1820)

West's life is a remarkable success story, even when one discounts the apotheosizing tendencies of his first biographer, John Galt. Born of Quaker parents on a farm near Springfield, Chester County, Pennsylvania, and with little formal education, Benjamin West became royal painter to George III before his thirty-fifth year; two decades later he was President of the Royal Academy in London, a post he held for all but one year from 1792 to his death in 1820, when "he was buried beside Reynolds, Opie, and Barry in St. Paul's Cathedral, his pall being borne by noblemen, ambassadors, and academicians; his two sons and grandson were chief mourners; and sixty coaches brought up the splendid procession."

But in his life, a simplicity and directness of language and deportment, related partially, at least, to his Quaker upbringing, led him to decline the honor of knighthood, saying, "I really think that I have earned greater eminence by my pencil already than a knighthood could confer on me."

Despite his long residence and his great success in England, West remained essentially American in a sense that some of the late nineteenth-century expatriates did not. His studio in London was always open to American artists, and he trained three generations of American artists, among them Peale and Stuart, Sully and Allston, Trumbull and Morse.

As a youth, West had shown precocious artistic talent, but his father had religious qualms about allowing the boy to follow the profession of painter. The Quaker prohibition was based on the theory that the fine arts were "only to embellish pleasures and to strengthen our inducements to gratify the senses at the expense of our immortal claims." His father therefore brought the matter before the local Society of Friends, asking them publicly what the destiny of his son ought to be. Galt reports that after a debate approaching altercation, a Quaker rose and delivered an eloquent speech, ending with the statement, "It is true that our tenets deny the utility of that art to mankind. But God has bestowed on the youth a genius for the art, and can we believe that Omniscience bestows His gifts but for great purposes? What God has given, who shall dare to throw away?" The Quaker carried the day, and young West began his training.

A productive career followed; William Dunlap estimated that West's more than 400 paintings and drawings would cover a wall 10 feet high and a quarter of a mile long.

West assimilated and is part of the long academic tradition of art mediated by Reynolds and going back to the Renaissance. This tradition represents a particular moral passion in which art, religion, and love of country are intertwined. In a letter to Charles Willson Peale, West said, in part: "…the art of painting has powers to dignify man, by transmitting to posterity his noble actions, and his mental powers, to be viewed in those invaluable lessons of religion, love of country, and morality." *Reference:* (1) John Galt, *The Life, Studies, and Works of Benjamin West, Esq.,* London, 1820. Reprinted 1960, Gainesville, Florida; (2) William Dunlap, *The History of the Rise and Progress of the Arts of Design in the United States,* Vol. I, New York, 1834. Reprinted 1969, Dover Publications, New York; (3) Grose Evans, *Benjamin West and the Taste of His Times,* Carbondale, Illinois, 1959.

*10. Benjamin West. *Seated Pilgrim.* (n.d.). Oil on canvas. 19⅞ x 17¾". The Museum of Fine Arts, Houston: Gift of the Family of Joseph S. Cullinan.

The *Seated Pilgrim* is enigmatic in regard to subject and to the large body of West's work. The attributes of the old man—staff and cape, hat with turned-back brim, and cockle shell—are all associated with the pilgrims of St. James. This pilgrim is dispiritedly seated, head resting on one hand, brows drawn together, in contrast to traditional saints and pilgrims, who may be portrayed in suffering, but not in despair.

The pervasive mood of dejection, fatigue, and quietude in this painting is also unusual in West's work, as is the meticulous attention to detail. It is possible that the painting may once have been slightly larger, with additional details which would assist in identifying the subject more precisely.

11. Benjamin West. *Hagar and Ishmael.* 1780 (or 1789?). Pen, sepia, blue wash. 17½ x 20¼". Addison Gallery of American Art, Phillips Academy, Andover, Massachusetts.

The story of Hagar and Ishmael was often treated by nineteenth-century artists, perhaps because it evokes emotions that appealed to early nineteenth-century sensibilities—pity for the unjustly rejected, motherly love, and awe in the presence of divine intervention. Hagar, the Egyptian concubine of Abraham, was driven out of Abraham's home by Sarah together with Ishmael, the son of Hagar and Abraham. Abraham, having been instructed by God that he will make a nation of the son of the slave-woman, took Hagar and Ishmael and left them in the wilderness of Beer-sheba. When Hagar's water was gone she put the child under a bush, praying: " 'Let me not look upon the death of the child'…and the angel of God called to Hagar from the heaven, and said to her, 'What troubles you, Hagar? Fear not; for God has heard the voice of the lad where he is. Arise, lift up the lad, and hold him fast with your hand; for I will make him a great nation.' Then God opened her eyes and she saw a well of water…"

West's drawing may be related to his painting of this subject owned by the Metropolitan Museum. The postures and expressions of all three figures differ in the Metropolitan painting, but we know that these were changed by West between the first painting of it in 1776 and the repainting completed by 1803.

12. Benjamin West. *The Wise Men's Offering.* 1799. Oil on canvas. 50 x 23½". Courtesy Kennedy Galleries, Inc., New York: Collection Mr. and Mrs. Richard Manney, Irvington, New York.

As royal painter to George III, West was invited by the King to plan a cycle of paintings, "a great work on Revealed Religion," for a private chapel the King intended to build at Windsor. West arranged the several subjects in "four Dispensations" and in his account book wrote, "His Majesty was pleased to approve the arrangement selected, as did several of the Bishops in whose hands he placed them for their consideration, and they highly approved the same." Thus, both the subjects and their novel division in this form were apparently West's own conception.

West's list contains the Antediluvian Dispensation (three paintings); the Patriarchal Dispensation (four paintings); the Mosaical Dispensation (ten paintings); and last, the Dispensation of the Prophets, which includes among its nineteen paintings *The Wise Men's Offering*, a sketch for a stained-glass window intended for the chapel's west end. Its fresh and spontaneous brushwork and fluidity of forms distinguish it from the finished paintings for the chapel.

The illness of George III terminated the project, and West's paintings were dispersed in England and the United States. An impressive group of the Dispensation paintings is owned by Bob Jones University, Greenville, South Carolina.

Reference: John Galt, *The Life, Studies, and Works of Benjamin West, Esq.,* London, 1820. Reprinted 1960, Gainesville, Florida.

13. Benjamin West. *Christ Healing the Sick in the Temple.* (1774/reworked 1794?). Oil on canvas. 29¼ x 46¼". M. H. deYoung Memorial Museum, San Francisco: Gift of Mr. David Pleydell-Bouverie.

This is a sketch for the large composition which West presented to the Pennsylvania Hospital in Philadelphia as "a noble memorial of his love to the country of his birth, and her institutions." The painting, exhibited in London, was received with enormous enthusiasm and an offer for it of 3,000 guineas which West accepted, stipulating that he would make a copy for the hospital in Philadelphia.

The copy was sent to the United States; contrary to West's expectations, the trustees of the hospital charged admission to view the painting, and made $4,000 during the first year. Subsequently the painting toured the country; a publication called *The Bee* reports (21 February 1844) its being exhibited at the Cathedral in New Orleans and that 40,000 people had paid twenty-five cents each for the privilege of seeing it.

The peripatetic Charles Dickens, who saw the painting in Philadelphia, stated that it was exhibited for the financial benefit of the institution and "...is perhaps as favourable a specimen of the master as can be seen anywhere," adding circumspectly, "Whether this be high or low praise, depends upon the reader's taste."

The sketch focuses upon the unusually tall figure of Jesus, with its sharp contrasts and sustained rhythms. The melodramatic mood of those crowding about the majestic figure of Christ is characteristic of the early phases of Romanticism.
Reference: William Dunlap, *The History of the Rise and Progress of the Arts of Design in the United States,* Vol. I, New York, 1834. Reprinted 1969, Dover Publications, New York.

14. Benjamin West. *Ascension of Christ.* 1798. Oil on canvas. 21¾ x 14¼". Washington County Museum of Fine Arts, Hagerstown, Maryland.

In this oil sketch, Christ is only partially visible in the upper left zone, attended by angels. The groups at the lower left and right are the Apostles, Mary, and several women followers. The composition is entirely dominated by two commanding central figures, the two men referred to in Acts I:11 who stood by them in white robes and said, "Men of Galilee, why do you stand looking into heaven? This Jesus, who was taken up from you into heaven, will come in the same way as you saw him go into heaven."

The central figure is reminiscent of the Apollo Belvedere, the classical statue most revered by artists and connoisseurs of the eighteenth century. It was the first classical statue to be seen by the 22-year-old West when he arrived in Rome in July, 1760. The news spread quickly that an American Quaker had come to study the fine arts in Italy. It was arranged for the young Quaker to see "the chef d'oeuvres of antiquity" in the presence of the sophisticated group about Cardinal Albani. West's immediate response to the Apollo Belvedere was, "How like a young Mohawk warrior!"—an exclamation which at first mortified his distinguished audience, until he explained the physical characteristics of the Mohawks and how he had seen a warrior in the same attitude as the Apollo, "intensely pursuing with his eye the flight of the arrow just discharged from the bow." His audience, in Dunlap's words, "applauded his untutored acumen."
Reference: William Dunlap, *The History of the Rise and Progress of the Arts of Design in the United States,* New York, 1834. Reprinted 1969, Dover Publications, New York.

*15. Benjamin West. *Elijah Convincing the False Prophets of Baal.* 1798. Oil on paper mounted on panel. 31 x 22". Mead Art Building, Amherst College, Amherst, Massachusetts.

Benjamin West, like his contemporaries Fuseli and Blake, painted scenes of sorcery and horror with a fervor that is often spine-tingling. In this oil sketch, West shows the climax of the grisly contest between Elijah and the prophets of Baal (I Kings 18:20–40) when each sacrificed a bull, cut it in pieces and laid it upon an altar, and then called upon their gods, agreeing that the god who answered by fire would indeed be God. The prophets of Baal called upon their gods from morning to noon with no response. But when Elijah invoked the Lord God of Abraham, Isaac and Israel, "then the fire of the Lord fell, and consumed the burnt offering, and the wood, and the stones, and the dust, and licked up the water that was in the trench. And when all the people saw it, they fell on their faces; and they said, 'The Lord, he is God; the Lord, he is God.'"

A mighty angel who pulls a sword from its case rippling with flame, is the bearer of the fire of God in West's dramatic vision of the climax of the contest.

*16. Benjamin West. *The Angel in the Sun.* (ca. 1800). Wash drawing. 11 x 13½". The Toledo Museum of Art: Gift of Edward Drummond Libbey.

This drawing, listed by West in his account book as "The Angel in the Sun assembling the Birds of the Air, before the destruction of the Old Beast," vibrates with apocalyptic energy. The passage in the Book of Revelation reads: "Then I saw an angel standing in the sun, and with a loud voice he called to all the birds that fly in midheaven, 'Come, gather for the great supper of God, to eat the flesh of kings, the flesh of captains, the flesh of mighty men, the flesh of horses and their riders, and the flesh of all men, both free and slave, both small and great.'" The Angel leaps toward us, arm raised in a gesture of command, hair blown aside, his wings, and cape and billowing garment in taut opposing curves. The Angel has, in fact, three right legs but rather than obtruding, the additional leg seems to underline the dynamic movement of the figure.

In view of his Quaker background, it is interesting to note West's attraction for subject matter which is apocalyptic, fantastic, grotesque, or that which has the elements of horror.

*17. Benjamin West. *Death on a Pale Horse.* (1802). Oil on canvas. 21 x 36″. Philadelphia Museum of Art: Given by Theodora Kimball Hubbard, in memory of Edwin Fiske Kimball.

"Then I saw heaven opened, and behold, a white horse! He who sat upon it is called Faithful and True, and in righteousness he judges and makes war. His eyes are like a flame of fire, and on his head are many diadems; and he has a name inscribed which no one knows but himself. He is clad in a robe dipped in blood, and the name by which he is called is The Word of God." West depicts this vision, recorded in the Book of Revelation, with a dramatic fervor and baroque dynamism that makes the small canvas alive with surging movement. His contemporaries were greatly impressed by this sketch when it was shown in London and Paris in 1802. An earlier sketch of the same subject and the final composition, over 14 feet by 25 feet in size, is now permanently installed at the Pennsylvania Academy.

But it is this sketch which Washington Allston, just arrived in London to study painting, described in a letter to a friend in Charleston: "…a more sublime and awful picture I never beheld. It is impossible to conceive anything more terrible than Death on the white horse, and I am certain no painter has exceeded Mr. West in the fury, horror, and despair which he has represented in the surrounding figures." Allston, who admitted he had been strongly prejudiced against his compatriot West, was thus won over to proclaim that "among the many painters in London I should rank Mr. West as first" after seeing West's gallery, and this picture in particular.

Reference: Jared B. Flagg, *The Life and Letters of Washington Allston,* New York, 1892.

*18. Joshua Shaw. *The Deluge.* (ca. 1805). Oil on canvas. 48¼ x 66". The Metropolitan Museum of Art, New York: Gift of William Merritt Chase, 1909.

This scene of devastation is based on the account of the flood in Genesis 7: "The waters prevailed and increased greatly upon the earth...And all flesh died that moved upon the earth, birds, cattle, beasts, all swarming creatures that swarm upon the earth, and everyman; everything on the dry land in whose nostrils was the breath of life died." In a startling departure from the text, Shaw portrays the human beings already dead, while a dog and a few birds still live.

This painting is one of the first landscapes expressing the ambience of the sublime and the gloomy, a transformation of nature through the artist's own emotional involvement. A contemporary reviewer extolled "its grey solemnity, its rainy cataract, and heaving inundation of the great deep, burying the creation in a watery wreck; the terror-inspiring effect of the deluge is expressed by a novel and very natural circumstance of a dog standing on an elevated piece of ground near a drowned family, and howling as he looks up at the watery gloom."

The painting was originally attributed to Washington Allston and was widely exhibited and published as by him. Subsequently it was proven to be by Joshua Shaw, an artist born in England, who settled in Philadelphia in 1817.

Reference: Albert Ten Eyck Gardner and Stuart P. Feld, *American Paintings, A Catalogue...Painters born by 1815,* Vol. I, The Metropolitan Museum of Art, New York (ca. 1965).

William Dunlap says of Washington Allston that he was "number one" in the catalogue of American painters or at least only second to his great master and precursor, West. Dunlap goes on to say of the relationship between West and Allston, "the mantle of Elijah has fallen upon the shoulders of Elisha."

Possessed of unusual charm of mien and manner, Allston's influence as a person as well as a painter was felt in cultural circles in the first half of the nineteenth century. Something of the impact of the man is reflected in contemporaries' tributes. Horatio Greenough, the sculptor, counted himself among those "who owed to Allston the birth of their souls." And some years after his death, Longfellow wrote, "One man may sweeten a whole town. I never pass through Cambridgeport without thinking of Allston. His memory is the quince in the drawer, and perfumes the atmosphere."

Allston was educated in a school in his native Charleston, prepared for college at Newport, and went to Harvard, where he graduated with honors and was the class poet. After leaving college, he sold his share of the family property in order to finance his study abroad. In 1801 he sailed for England; from 1804 to 1808 he was in Italy, mostly in Rome. Here he first met Coleridge, who became a life-long friend. During his second stay in England and after the death of his first wife, Allston, like his friend Coleridge, joined the Episcopal church. In 1818 he was elected honorary member of the American Academy of Fine Arts and in the same year he returned to the United States, to live the rest of his life in Boston, Cambridge, and Cambridgeport. In 1827 his first exhibition was held at the Boston Athenaeum. In 1830 he married the sister of the poet Richard H. Dana and at his death in 1843 he was buried in the Dana vault in Cambridge.

During most of his career Allston wrote poetry and other literature; his *Lectures on Art* and collected aphorisms remain important documents of the time. Writing, and his active involvement with poet friends, perhaps give a clue to the attraction he felt for literary subjects evoking strong feelings. His most ambitious and important, if not always most successful, paintings are of Biblical episodes with complex narrative elements. The titles of two suggest this: *Jeremiah Dictating His Prophecy of the Destruction of Jerusalem to Baruch the Scribe* (ill. p.65) and *The Dead Man Revived by Touching the Bones of the Prophet Elisha* (now in the Pennsylvania Academy of Art). Allston's overwhelming preference for Old Testament subjects can also be noted in this context: *Saul and the Witch of Endor* (ill. p.67), *Rebecca at the Well, Jacob's Dream, Elijah in the Desert, David Playing before Saul, Miriam the Prophetess* and *Belshazzar's Feast.*

His New Testament subjects are few, many of them unfinished. He became dissatisfied with an oil sketch, *Christ Healing the Sick,* of which he wrote, "I may here observe that the universal failure of all painters, ancient and modern, in their attempts to give even a tolerable idea of the Saviour, has now determined me never to attempt it. Besides, I think his character too holy and sacred to be attempted by the pencil." The large canvas of the *Angel Releasing St. Peter from Prison* in the Boston Museum is one of his few extant completed paintings on a New Testament theme.

Reference: (1) William Dunlap, *The History of the Rise and Progress of the Arts of Design in the United States,* Vol. I, New York, 1834. Reprinted 1969, Dover Publications, New York; (2) Jared B. Flagg, *The Life and Letters of Washington Allston,* New York, 1892; (3) E. P. Richardson, *Washington Allston, A Study of the Romantic Artist in America,* New York, 1948.

19. Washington Allston. *Rebecca at the Well.* 1816. Oil on canvas. 29¾ x 35½". Fogg Art Museum, Harvard University, Cambridge, Massachusetts: The Washington Allston Trust, Mr. Henry L. de Rham, Trustee.

Rebecca at the Well was a subject popular with nineteenth-century painters, combining a romantic courtship with exotic landscapes and supernatural overtones. Abraham's servant, at the patriarch's instruction, set out to find a bride for Isaac. He took ten camels and choice gifts from his master and was instructed to go to the well outside the city of Nabor in Mesopotamia at the time of evening when the women go out to draw water. He was to ask for a drink from the daughters of the men of the city, and when he did, Rebecca, "a maiden fair to look upon, and a virgin, said 'Drink, my lord' and she quickly let down her jar upon her hand, and gave him a drink." Allston portrays this moment of recognition on the part of Abraham's servant and the innocent charity on the part of Rebecca. Allston has focused on the graceful stance of the radiant young Rebecca and the watchful, hopeful gaze and slightly tremulous kneeling servant. The Poussin-like landscape setting, with its easy recession into successive planes of depth, shows Allston's great skill as a landscape artist.

*20. Washington Allston. *The Prophet Jeremiah Dictating to his Scribe Baruch.* 1820. Oil on canvas. 89¾ x 62¾". Yale University Art Gallery, New Haven, Connecticut: Gift of S. F. B. Morse, B.A. 1810.

Allston referred to this painting as "one of the grandest compositions I have made." It was a commission but was eventually purchased by the artist-inventor Samuel F. B. Morse, who presented it to Yale College in 1866.

In its more than human scale, its ponderous volumes, and the high seriousness of the entire conception, it represents a side of Washington Allston's work quite different from the pastoral, idyllic character of the *Rebecca,* or the harmonious landscapes Allston painted in his earlier years. The figure of Jeremiah has certainly been influenced both by Michelangelo's representation of the Prophet on the Sistine ceiling and by his statue of Moses.

The massive figure sits "lost in mysterious communion with the divine Being," wrote a contemporary commentator. "Never did I feel so distinctly the nigh approach of a heavenly power, or contemplate the inward emotions of the soul so entirely abstracted from all that is bodily. Jeremiah is a gigantic figure; yet you do not think of him as such...He is looking beyond all earthly things, into the infinite distance, and the invisible is made visible to him." The writer piously concludes: "I wish I felt at liberty to tell Mr. Allston how grateful I am to him for having shown me one of the prophets of old, and for having sent me away a more thoughtful and religious man."

Reference: Jared B. Flagg, *The Life and Letters of Washington Allston,* New York, 1892.

*21. Washington Allston. *Saul and the Witch of Endor.* (1820). Oil on canvas. 34 x 47″. Mead Art Building, Amherst College, Amherst, Massachusetts.

For twentieth-century sensibilities, this strange painting borders on bathos rather than the high seriousness which the artist intended. Allston portrays the moment that the Witch of Endor, having raised Samuel and recognized Saul, cries out against the king knowing herself deceived by him; Saul had previously banished all witches and wizards on pain of death.

The witch, reminiscent of Michelangelo's sibyls, gestures with an odd and ineffectual movement; Saul stares at her and apparently cannot see the apparition she has conjured up at his insistence. The vision of Samuel hangs above billows of supposedly supernatural smoke. His actions, like those of the Witch and Saul, seem staged. We sense a disjunction between the emotions that Allston intended to express and the melodramatic character of the gestures and facial expressions which should convey them.

William Sidney Mount was born and died on Long Island, and lived there most of his life. At seventeen years of age he learned the trade of sign painting from his older brother. He briefly studied at the National Academy School with Henry Inman, but soon returned to Stony Brook. In 1828 he exhibited his painting of *Christ Raising the Daughter of Jarius* at the National Academy and thereafter was a regular exhibitor, becoming a full member of the Academy in 1832. Between 1829 and 1836 he took up portrait painting and lived in New York City. But in 1836 he returned to Stony Brook and made it his permanent home. Despite offers from Luman Reed and his son-in-law to pay the expenses, Mount never went abroad. He traveled very little in this country. A trip to see Thomas Cole, whose painting he greatly admired, or a trip up the Hudson, marked the extent of his journeying.

Alfred Frankenstein, who has studied the many voluminous diaries, notebooks, journals, and letters which Mount was forever scribbling found a brief entry in an undated diary in the Smithtown Library:

> Presbyterianism how cold and ridged. When Sunday should have been a day of happyness, it was to me under blue skies decipline, a day of gloom. I was pleased when the sun went down and often dreaded when Sunday came, for the thoughts of eternal damnation and brimstone was to be raked over, which to my mind seemed strange when I could not discover anything in nature to bare the doctrine out.

Mount had a serious interest in spiritualism, a movement which began in the 1840s and which had gathered considerable momentum by 1854. Mount's notes include a record of a seance in which he asked the spirit "how should we best worship God?" receiving the answer, "By following the stringent dictates of your own conscience." It is interesting to note that the artist William Rimmer, a younger contemporary of Mount's, was also involved in spiritualism, and was deemed by some of his contemporaries to have the clairvoyance and powers of a medium.

Although his *Saul and the Witch of Endor* and *Christ Raising the Daughter of Jarius*, both done in his first year as a painter, are the only religious subjects now known to be by Mount, the Karolik Collection of the Museum of Fine Arts, Boston, has a sheet dated 1867 which has some twenty pencil sketches in matchbox size, some of which are clearly ideas for religious subjects —one central sketch shows Christ blessing a child, another shows Christ at Gethsemane returning to his sleeping apostles and is inscribed "sleep on"; another appears to be an Eve leaning indolently against the tree, her head at one side as if listening to the serpent.

Reference: (1) Alfred Frankenstein, *Painter of Rural America: William Sidney Mount,* Suffolk Museum at Stony Brook, Long Island, 1968; (2) Alfred Frankenstein, "William Sidney Mount and the Art of Painting," *American Art Journal,* I:1, Spring, 1969.

*22. William Sidney Mount. *Saul and the Witch of Endor.* 1828. Oil on canvas. 35⅞ x 48″. National Collection of Fine Arts, Smithsonian Institution, Washington, D.C.

According to the artist, this melodramatic composition was his third painting. Its subject, like that of Allston's (ill.p.67) is I Samuel 28:7–14. The histrionic and rhetorical gestures, the foreshortenings, the draperies, and the harshness of color all betray the beginner's hand and eye. Mount was certainly influenced by Benjamin West's painting of the same subject, which he may have known from an engraving.

"T. Bailey, Esq.", who bought this picture from Mount for twenty dollars, was the renowned Navy officer, Theodorus Bailey (1805–1877), whose portrait Mount was to paint (for seventy-five dollars) in October, 1852. Shortly thereafter, on December 28, 1852, Bailey wrote Mount telling him of the attraction the Witch of Endor painting held for him. Bailey went on to require of Mount a complete curriculum of his artistic development in both style and technique, "In short...a brief history of your life as connected with painting."

To this Mount replied, on January 5, 1853:

> Your kind note requesting me to furnish you with materials of myself "as connected with painting"...Now Capt. that is asking a little too much—why it would take me three months to shell it all out—to clean the cob all off, and who would feed me with pudding and milk all that while? Echo answers who.

Reference: Alfred Frankenstein, *Painter of Rural America 1807–1868,* The International Exhibitions Foundation, 1968.

23. Rembrandt Peale. *The Court of Death.* (Copyright 1859). Hand-colored lithograph. 15¼ x 26⅝″. Library of Congress, Washington, D.C.: Prints and Photographs Division.

This is a lithograph after Rembrandt Peale's immense (eleven feet high x twenty-three feet long) and popular painting, *The Court of Death.* The painting toured cities of the eastern seaboard, where over 30,000 Americans paid a total of $9,000 to see it. Ministers made it the subject of their sermons, and many people bought colored lithographs, like the one exhibited, for a dollar apiece. Peale said that his intention in painting it was to "render useful the rational contemplation of death," and to present a morally illuminating sermon in paint. In a letter of December 1, 1845, he explained that the inspiration for the painting was Bishop Porteus' poem on death, which so caught his imagination that he immediately prepared a larger painting room in which to execute it, and did innumerable studies from life of figures, heads, and hands. He used friends, relatives, passers-by, and a cadaver as models, and concludes:

> Thus was my Picture produced, and was intended as a "Discourse on Life and Death"—and I had the satisfaction to find that it could be understood, by the unlearned and the learned...I would lay claim to some little credit for the stand I took in reprobation of Intemperance, before that subject was introduced to popular notice; and the Society of Friends, at least, will give me credit for my views of the Glory and Magnanimity of War; whilst the philosophic Christian must agree with the picture that Death has no terror in the eyes of Virtuous Old Age, and of Innocence, Faith and Hope.

Reference: John W. McCoubrey, *American Art 1700–1960, Sources and Documents,* Englewood Cliffs, New Jersey, 1965.

Horatio Greenough (1805–1852)

Horatio Greenough was the first American to make sculpture his profession and to gain international recognition thereby. He was born in Boston and began his career copying casts of classical sculptures at the Boston Athenaeum. His friendship with Washington Allston, begun while at Harvard, influenced his career and his thought. After graduating from Harvard in 1824, Greenough went to Carrara and later settled in Florence, where he and James Fenimore Cooper became close friends. Through the influence of Allston and Daniel Webster, in 1832 Greenough was given the first important commission by the U.S. government to an artist, for a statue of George Washington.

Greenough's religious background seems to have been Unitarian. His family rented a pew in the First Congregational Society, then Unitarian, and he studied at Harvard during the ascendancy of Unitarianism there. In addition to the sculpture in this exhibition, his other works with religious themes are another bust of *Christ,* a *Dead Abel,* a relief of *St. John Forbidding the Angel to Worship Him,* the *Angel Abdiel,* and two versions of *David.*

Greenough's theory and observations were published in *The Travels, Observations and Experiences of a Yankee Stonecutter.* Most seminal of his theories, especially for later designers and architects, was his principle that "form follows function." In his original statement of the theory it is seen as the Creator's formula: "If there be any principle of structure more plainly inculcated in the works of the Creator than all others, it is, the principle of unflinching adaptation of forms to functions."

Greenough had an easy, engaging personality and was a part of the intellectual and artistic life of whatever place he lived, whether Boston, Florence, or Rome. On November 21, 1852, Emerson gave a dinner honoring the English poet Clough: Horatio Greenough was invited, and the roster of other guests gives us a picture of that brilliant circle who were his contemporaries and friends—Hawthorne, Longfellow, James Russell Lowell, Theodore Parker, Sumner, Samuel Ward, and Ellery Channing. This may have been one of the last social functions Greenough attended for slightly over a month later he died of brain fever.

Reference: (1) Nathalia Wright, *Horatio Greenough, The First American Sculptor,* University of Pennsylvania Press, Philadelphia, 1963; (2) Wayne Craven, *Sculpture in America,* New York, 1968; (3) Henry T. Tuckerman, *A Memorial of Horatio Greenough,* New York 1853.

24. Horatio Greenough. *The Ascension of a Child Conducted by an Infant Angel.* 1832. Marble. 30⅛ x 22½ x 14". Museum of Fine Arts, Boston: Gift of Laurence Curtis.

Greenough's original title for this sculptural group was *Journey to Heaven* and he described it as a "contrast between the ideal forms and face of the cherub and the milky fatness and shew-baby, half doubting, half pleased look of the child." Samuel Cabot, the Boston merchant who had commissioned the sculpture, objected at first to Greenough's wish to "make them both stark naked," but as Greenough reported, he "fought hard and carried the day—the little fellows are to be provided with alabaster fig leaves which shall fall at a tap! of the hammer when the discerning public shall have *digested* the fruit of the knowledge of good and evil." We obviously see them as Greenough intended. The base is incised with Greenough's name, the date 1832, and with a Latin inscription, *"Quae nunc Abibis in Loca?"* ("To what place will you go now?")

   The sculpture was shown in a special exhibition in Boston and the receipts went to Father Edward Taylor's Charities for Seamen's Children, in which the patron, Samuel Cabot, was interested. Unlike an earlier sculpture of two nude children by Greenough, this group did not provoke shocked or flippant reactions. The alabaster leaves served their purpose, it seems. *Reference:* Nathalia Wright, *Horatio Greenough, The First American Sculptor,* University of Pennsylvania Press, Philadelphia, 1963.

*25. Horatio Greenough. *Christ.* (ca. 1845–1846). Marble. 32 x 18 x 13", irreg. Courtesy of the Trustees of the Boston Public Library.

*26. Horatio Greenough. *Lucifer.* (ca. 1841–1842). Marble. 33 x 15 x 12″, irreg. Courtesy of the Trustees of the Boston Public Library.

The busts of Lucifer and Christ are counterparts; the contrast between the turbulent Lucifer, portrayed after his fall, and the serene symmetrical Christ is quite deliberate. Lucifer is the Romantic, Byronic type of Satan. A contemporary of Greenough's who visited his studio commented about this statue:

> …in marble, is a head of Lucifer, of colossal size. The countenance has the beauty of an archangel, with the hard, uncertain look of an archangel fallen…The sinister nature lies concealed, as it were in the features, and comes out gradually, after they have been sometime contemplated.

The head of Christ recalls Michelangelo's Christ of his early *Pietá,* a debt made even clearer in Greenough's later bust of Christ owned by the Fogg Art Museum. The didactic and moralistic treatment of the subject is attested to by Greenough himself, who referred to the present sculpture in a letter:

> I am not aware that any American has, until now, risked the placing before his countrymen a representation of Our Saviour. The strong prejudice, or rather conviction of the Protestant mind has, perhaps, deterred many. Not behind the most jealous in deprecating the abuse of images in places of public worship, I think, nevertheless, that the person and face of Our Saviour is a legitimate subject of art, because, although our conception must fall short of what the heart of the Christian looks for, yet you will allow that we may offer to many an imperfect instead of a mean or grovelling idea which they have drawn from other sources. The prayers and hymns of the most pious are as far unworthy the perfection to which they are addressed, as the lights and shadows of the artist; yet both may be accepted as fervent aspirations after the good and beautiful. It is a mistake to suppose that the artist, because he stops working, thinks his task perfect; he says only—behold the subject proposed to me as the art which is in me can give it.

Reference: (1) Henry T. Tuckerman, *Book of the Artists,* New York, 1867; reprinted by James F. Carr, New York, 1966; (2) Henry T. Tuckerman, *A Memorial to Horatio Greenough,* New York, 1853.

*27. Thomas Crawford. *Adam and Eve.* 1855. Marble. 53½ x 25 x 28". Boston Athenaeum.

Adam, referred to so frequently and with such complex meanings in American literature, is seen in surprisingly few works of nineteenth-century art. This sculpture is one of the few examples of a portrayal of Adam. Although many nineteenth-century sculptures exist in multiple copies, Crawford's *Adam and Eve* appears to be unique. Loaned and then given to the Athenaeum after being exhibited there in 1865, it is now more than one hundred years since the sculpture has been seen outside those walls.

Could the elder Henry James have seen Crawford's sculpture? Writing in 1857, he deplored what he termed "the sleek and comely Adamic condition," as if man were to remain "a mere dimpled nursling of the skies" undisturbed "by those fierce storms of the intellect . . . but also unvisited by a single glimpse of the Divine and halcyon calm of the heart in which these hideous storms will finally rock themselves to sleep."

Crawford, born in New York City, served an apprenticeship with wood-carvers and then worked with stonecutters. He went to Italy in 1835, studied in Rome with Thorwaldsen, and eventually received the most important commission given to any American sculptor of the time, the execution of the sculptural decorations of the Capitol. Tuckerman relates that Crawford was an Episcopalian and lists among his works "a series of Christian or religious illustrations, from Adam and Saul to Christ and the woman at the well of Samaria."

Reference: (1) R. W. B. Lewis, *The American Adam: Innocence, Tragedy, and Tradition in the Nineteenth Century,* Chicago, 1955; (2) Henry T. Tuckerman, *Book of the Artists,* New York, 1867.

William Page was born in Albany, and at the age of fifteen studied painting in New York with James Herring and then with Samuel F. B. Morse. In 1827 he joined the Presbyterian church, his father having been a firm Protestant. Shortly thereafter he entered Phillips Academy at Andover, Massachusetts, to study for the ministry, but left after a few months. His career as a painter centered first in New York (1835–1843), then in Boston (1844–1847), then in Florence and Rome. In Florence and Rome, Page became an important member of the expatriate group which included Robert and Elizabeth Barrett Browning, as well as the American sculptor Hiram Powers.

In a letter to John Ruskin, Mrs. Browning described Page as "an earnest, simple, noble artist and man, who carries his Christianity down from his deepest heart to the point of his brush." Mrs. Browning and Page were both interested in spiritualism and in "spirit writing." Concurrently with his interest in spiritualism, Page discovered Swedenborg in Florence. Joshua Taylor states, "Page's already firmly established belief in a correspondence between the natural and the spiritual order, the ways of spiritualism were simply further confirmation…In his early efforts…there was a general groping toward a spiritual content; in his works now the effect was conscious and intensified. Every line, every color, now had a dual purpose: to represent with accuracy the perfect forms of nature and to evoke directly through the emotions an awareness of spiritual being."

Although few of Page's religious paintings have survived, he painted a large canvas of *Moses, Aaron, and Hur on Mount Horeb* (a subject suggested by James Russell Lowell, a friend since their first meeting in 1840), a *Ruth and Naomi*, a *Holy Family*, a *Visitation*, and an *Ecce Homo*, now lost, which twentieth-century eyes might view differently from the contemporary critic, writing in 1843:

> This is evidently a labored effort of the artist, and yet he has succeeded in pleasing very few. The objections generally made, are to the rainbow halo, round the head—to the coarseness of the hands—the red coarse whiskers, but chiefly to the expression of the countenance. It is so *human.* There is an appearance of mental suffering, and the face possesses a good deal of character, such as the artist intended to give it, but that character conflicts with all our preconceived notions of the Being he has represented. There is nothing Godlike—nothing of the divinity—nothing of the high mission on which he was sent, which ought to make his face sublime. The general effect of the picture is ruined by the naked shoulder and the preponderance of red color in so much of the purple robe.

Although Page's contemporary critic deprecates what he sees as a lack of divinity his final comment grants Page his unique vision and skill, saying, "It is, however, such a picture as few artists but Page could paint."

Reference: Joshua C. Taylor, *William Page, The American Titian,* Chicago, 1957.

*28. William Page. *Flight into Egypt.* (ca. 1857–1859). Oil on canvas. 36 x 72". Kennedy Galleries, Inc., New York.

The first version of the *Flight into Egypt,* painted in Rome, was lost at sea. Page had retained a tracing of the composition and from it executed the present larger version, which was finished in 1859.

Joshua Taylor, who wrote the definitive work on Page, comments, "It is an unusual painting, with its quiet, somber mood, evoking a sense of expectation at the same time it establishes a feeling of tranquility...One surprising aspect of the painting is the appearance of Joseph. Instead of the traditional elder in flowing robes, he is a vigorous, muscular figure, suggesting in his alert stance the Vatican's standing discus-thrower which Page had studied with such care. It is Joseph who braves the barren expanse of new country while Mary docilely follows."
Reference: Joshua C. Taylor, *William Page: The American Titian,* Chicago, 1957.

29. Daniel Huntington. *Philosophy and Christian Art.* (1868). Oil on canvas. 40 x 50". Los Angeles County Museum of Art: Gift of Will Richeson.

Tuckerman recounts that Daniel Huntington "felt himself destined for a religious painter" from childhood. Huntington had studied at Hamilton College and then at the National Academy. He was apparently proficient in landscape and portrait painting, and "to those mechanical aptitudes," according to Tuckerman, "was added the inspiration of Faith."

Among Huntington's paintings with religious subjects, Tuckerman describes one called *The Sacred Lesson,* which has similarities to *Philosophy and Christian Art.* In it, an old man with "an expression of calm and holy wisdom" uses a missal of some sort to instruct a girl "with an ingenuous and innocent countenance, from which beams a look of meek inquiry and sweet confidence." *Philosophy and Christian Art* implies a dialogue between reason represented by the old sage and his book with mathematical symbols at the left, and intuition embodied by the young woman. Intuition is associated with art (the painting of the Adoration of the Shepherds which she points to) and nature (the view behind her).

The title of the present painting has varied; in the National Academy of Design show in 1869 it was listed as *Science and Christian Art;* in a Paris exhibition of 1878 it was titled *Philosophy and Religion.*
Reference: Henry T. Tuckerman, *Book of the Artists,* New York, 1867 (reprinted, New York, 1966).

Group III

*30. Betsy B. Lathrop. *Japhthah's Return.* 1812. Watercolor on silk. 22 x 25¾". Abby Aldrich Rockefeller Folk Art Collection, Williamsburg, Virginia.

Although this blithe scene might be an illustration for a romance, in fact the episode is tragic. The knight is Jephthah, the victorious leader who had defeated the Ammonites, and had vowed to give as a burnt offering to the Lord whatever he first saw coming out of the door of his house: "Jephthah came to his home at Mizpah; and behold, his daughter came out to meet him with timbrels and with dances; she was his only child... And when he saw her, he rent his clothes and said, 'Alas, my daughter...'" (Judges II:34).

The details of the painting derive both from the young artist's observations of her own contemporaries, and from prints she had seen. The building rendered in some detail in the background is probably based on a print of the Moorish Gothic temple, a folly built at Stowe, Buckinghamshire, England.

Reference: (1) Mary Black and Jean Lipman, *American Folk Painting,* New York, 1966; (2) William P. Campbell, *101 American Primitive Water Colors and Pastels from the Collection of William and Bernice Chrysler Garbisch,* Washington, D.C., National Gallery of Art, 1966.

31. Mary Ann Willson. *The Prodigal Son Taking Leave of his Father.* (ca. 1815). Pen and watercolor. 12⅞ x 10⅛". National Gallery of Art, Washington, D.C.: Gift of Edgar William and Bernice Chrysler Garbisch, 1964.

32. Mary Ann Willson. *The Prodigal Son Wasted his Substance.* (ca. 1815). Pen and watercolor. 12⅝ x 10″. National Gallery of Art, Washington, D.C.: Gift of Edgar William and Bernice Chrysler Garbisch, 1964.

****33.** Mary Ann Willson. *The Prodigal Son in Misery.* (ca. 1815). Pen and watercolor. 12½ x 10⅛″. National Gallery of Art, Washington, D.C.: Gift of Edgar William and Bernice Chrysler Garbisch, 1964.

34. Mary Ann Willson. *The Prodigal Son Reclaimed.* (ca. 1815). Pen and watercolor. 12⅝ x 10". National Gallery of Art, Washington, D.C.: Gift of Edgar William and Bernice Chrysler Garbisch, 1964.

Mary Ann Willson was a water-colorist who lived in Greenville Green, New York, and was active during the period 1800–1825. This vigorous, imaginative, ingenuous group of drawings is a very free appropriation of designs and motifs based on a series of engravings of 1814 by the American engraver, Amos Doolittle. A glimpse of Mary Ann Willson's life and viewpoint is found in a notice, signed "An admirer of art," which gives a contemporary account of Miss Willson at work:

> The Artist Miss Willson & her friend Miss Brundage came from one of the Eastern States and made their home in the town of Greenville Green, Cº. N.Y., bought a few acres & built, or found their house, made of logs, on the land, & where they resided many years—, One was the farmer and cultivated the land by the aid of neighbours occasionally doing some ploughing for them, this one planted & reaped & gathered in, while the other *Made pictures* which she sold to the farmers and others as rare and unique "works of art"—, their paints or colours were of the simplest kinds, berries, bricks, & occasional "Store paint" made up their wants for these elegant designs.
>
> These two maids left their home in the East with a romantic attachment for each other, and which continued until the death of the "farmer Maid." The Artist was inconsolable and after a brief time removed to parts unknown.
>
> The writer of this, often visited them—and takes great pleasure in testifying to their great simplicity & originality of character—their unqualified belief that these "picters" were very beautiful, (and original they certainly were) & boasting how greatly they were in demand, "Why! they go way to Canada and clear to Mobile"—They had not the slightese idea how ridiculous they were—Their perfect simplicity and honest earnestness made them & their "works" more interesting:—sui generis without design,
>
> The writer of this little sketch does not mean to compare these mineral & vegetable compounds of fantastic taste—with the more modern artistic works of a Cole,—Durand, Huntingdon & others—but simply as the work of a native artist—uneducated of course, but a *proof* of the unnecessary waste of time under old Masters; and Italian travel...

Reference: M. and M. Karolik Collection of American Water Colors and Drawings, 1800–1875, 2 vols., Boston, 1962.

35. Charles Willson Peale. *Noah and his Ark.* (1819). Oil on canvas. 40¾ x 50½". Pennsylvania Academy of the Fine Arts, Philadelphia.

Peale's *Noah and his Ark* is not an original composition, but is in fact an altered copy of a painting by an English artist which belonged to the Chief of Ordnance of the United States Army. After hearing John Trumbull praise the painting, Peale arranged to have it for a time and perhaps because of his interest in animals and natural history, immediately wrote to the owner for permission to copy it.

Upon starting work in October 1819, he wrote to his son, Titian Peale, that he had worked on it for seven weeks. "... I took some liberty in the copy, leaving out the enormous Elk on the left hand, it being too large for the ground it was placed on, & I substituted the American Buffalo in its place, & I added an Ass next to the Horse, whose belly in the original made a parrallell line with the Zebra's back. In everything else it [is as] faithful a copy as I could execute with the aid of high magnifying powers of spectacles."

Upon its completion, the painting was immediately hung in Charles Willson Peale's remarkable museum of natural history, which contained hundreds of animals and insects in the "habitat arrangements" still used by naturalists today.
Reference: Charles Coleman Sellers, "Charles Willson Peale with Patron and Populace," *Transaction of The American Philosophical Society,* 59(3):1969.

Edward Hicks, who is so closely associated with Quaker history, was not born a Quaker. His parents were Episcopalians and Tories. After his mother's death, he was brought up in the Twining home, a tranquil Pennsylvania Quaker farmstead. Hicks was apprenticed to a coach painter and earned his living at allied tasks. But he became interested in the Friends' ministry and in 1811 was recommended as minister by the Middletown Monthly Meeting. In 1815 he helped found Newtown Preparative Meeting, where he remained a member and minister the rest of his life. For a while he tried farming and failed. Thereafter his life was divided between the tasks of painting signs, "Index boards," street "directors," tavern signs, and touring the various Friends meetings as a preacher. In 1820 he began painting a gospel of peace and brotherly love in his *Peaceable Kingdoms,* giving them away to repay benefactors or pacify debtors. In 1827 the Separation of the Friends came, and Edward joined his cousin Elias Hicks in the Hicksite split away from the Orthodox group.

There are many extant variations on Hicks' theme, *The Peaceable Kingdom.* It is estimated that he may have done eighty paintings of the subject, at least forty of which exist today. Although the principal elements of the composition—the animals and the children and the distant group of William Penn and the Indians—remain the same, the arrangement of the groups, the size of the animals, and the mood and expression, shift dramatically in the paintings.

Hicks demeaned his pursuit of painting, saying that it was "one of those trifling, insignificant arts which has never been of substantial advantage to mankind." Yet, consonant with Quaker teachings, he wanted to avoid idleness and to do the work of which his mind was capable. Thus he endeavored to use his brush "within the bounds of innocence and usefulness."
Reference: (1) Edward Hicks, *Memoirs of the Life and Religious Labors of Edward Hicks, Late of Newtown, Bucks County, Pa.* Written by Himself, Philadelphia, 1851; (2) Alice Ford, *Edward Hicks: Painter of the Peaceable Kingdom,* Philadelphia, 1952.

*36. Edward Hicks. *Noah's Ark.* (1846). Oil on canvas. 26½ x 36¼". Philadelphia Museum of Art: Bequest of Lisa Norris Elkins.

Noah's Ark was modeled after the 1844 lithograph of the subject issued by Nathaniel Currier, a copy of which is still in the possession of Hicks' descendants. In one of the few references to painting contained in his *Memoirs,* Hicks, in his entry for the 18th of April, 1846, joked that he was a smarter workman than Noah in his ability to build an ark faster. His levity was short-lived; the same day he dismissed himself as "nothing but a poor worthless insignificant painter." Although the composition of *Noah's Ark* is modeled closely after the lithograph, the trees and shrubs, the lowering sky, the surging color, and the design and pattern of the animals transcend the source and make this painting one of the most beautiful of all his works. *Reference:* Alice Ford, *Edward Hicks, A Special Exhibition Devoted to His Life and Work,* Abby Aldrich Rockefeller Folk Art Collection, Williamsburg, Virginia, 1960.

37. Edward Hicks. *Peaceable Kingdom.* (ca. 1820–1830). Oil on canvas. 18¾ x 23½". Cleveland Museum of Art: Leonard Hanna Fund.

For the many *Peaceable Kingdoms* Hicks drew his theme from Isaiah, and paraphrased it, in his own verse: "The wolf shall with the lambkin / dwell in peace, / His grim carnivorous thirst for blood / shall cease, / The beauteous leopard with his restless eye, / Shall by the kid in perfect stillness lie; / The calf, the fatling, and young lion wild, / Shall all be led by one sweet little child."

This early version of the theme presents an interesting contrast to that of nineteen years later, owned by the St. Etienne Gallery (ill. p.89). In the Cleveland *Kingdom* there are fewer animals and only one child. Animals and humans are larger in size than their counterparts in the St. Etienne *Kingdom.* The animals, especially the ox and goat, are more naturalistic in this Cleveland version. And the leopard which stretches so prominently across the foreground of the St. Etienne *Kingdom* is not to be seen at all here. The Cleveland version is less cohesive as a composition, less expert in design, and more rural in mood.

***38.** Edward Hicks. *Peaceable Kingdom.* (1849). Oil on canvas. 24 x
30¼". Galerie St. Etienne, New York.

This painting, one of the last of Hicks' *Peaceable Kingdoms,* shows
Hicks' recurrent fascination with the leopard which, in earlier
versions of the painting, was confined to a smaller space. Here
his gaze toward the spectator is intensely focused and his body
flows across the canvas, dominating the foreground. In his
Memoirs, Hicks wrote of the leopard:

> The leopard is the most subtle, cruel, restless creature, and
> at the same time the most beautiful of all the carnivorous
> animals of the cat kind...men and women of this class in
> their sinful state, are not to be depended upon. Excessively
> fond of company, more especially where there is gaiety,
> music, and dancing, they frequent taverns and places of
> diversion, where young men too often become an easy
> prey to the demon of intemperance, and the poor nega-
> tively innocent female is too often seduced by these beauti-
> ful monsters, more cruel than the leopard...

Reference: Edward Hicks, *Memoirs of the Life and Religious Labors
of Edward Hicks, Late of Newtown, Bucks County, Pa.* Written by
Himself, Philadelphia, 1851.

Edward Hicks. *The Peaceable Kingdom with Quakers Bearing Banners* (detail). (n.d.). Oil on canvas. 17½ x 23½″. Yale University Art Gallery, New Haven, Connecticut: Bequest of Robert W. Carle, B.A. 1897. [Not in exhibition].

Edward Hicks. *The Peaceable Kingdom with Quakers Bearing Banners* (detail)

*39. Eward Hicks. *Peaceable Kingdom.* (ca. 1839). Oil on canvas. 17⅞ x 23¾". Friends Historical Library of Swarthmore College, Swarthmore, Pennsylvania.

There are several versions of *The Peaceable Kingdom with Quakers Bearing Banners.* This type of painting is sometimes referred to as the Kingdom of Conflict because it was painted at a time when the conflict within the Society of Friends, in which Edward Hicks was deeply involved, resulted in the great Separation of 1827. Under the influence of revivalism and the preaching of visiting English Quakers, the "Orthodox" group tended to stress the outward atonement of the historical Christ, and the Scriptures. Edward Hicks took the part of his cousin Elias Hicks, who was a leader in the emphasis on the mystical side of Quakerism. Edward Hicks' paintings of this time, instead of showing Penn's Treaty with the Indians in the background, show banner-bearing Quakers in the foreground, including cousin Elias Hicks and, in powdered wig, George Washington whom Edward Hicks greatly esteemed. Frederick B. Tolles has identified the three figures at the apex of the pyramid of Quakers as George Fox, William Penn, and Robert Barclay, the Quaker theologian. At the summit of the hill of the horizon are the twelve apostles with Christ at the center. A passage from a long poem by Edward Hicks seems to refer to the symbolism of the Quakers bearing a streamer from Calvary, or perhaps, as Eleanore Mather suggests, from Pendle Hill. "Sweet peace, the Saviour's legacy of love / Descended on them from the Heaven above. / Then mercy smiled and justice sat surrene, / While Heavenly glory filled the space between. / High on the mount, conspicuous to the sight, / Friends stood alone, environed round with light. / Then let them stand there, let the people know / They cannot mingle with the world below."

The deep erosions in the foreground landscape and the fierceness of the animals are viewed by Mary Black as expressions of the anxiety and grief felt by Hicks over the Separation. The linking of the substantial "cloud of witnesses" to the Light of Christ with a banner inscribed with a scriptural quotation associated with the birth of the historical Christ is, in Eleanore P. Mather's view, Hicks' answer to the Orthodox charge of heresy.

Reference: (1) Eleanore P. Mather, "Edward Hicks, Primitive Quaker," Pendle Hill Pamphlet 170, 1970; (2) Frederick B. Tolles, "The Primitive Painter as Poet (with an Attempted Solution of an Iconographic Puzzle in Certain of Edward Hicks' *Peaceable Kingdoms*)," Bulletin of the Friends Historical Association, Spring 1961, pp. 12–30; (3) Alice Ford, *Edward Hicks, A Special Exhibition Devoted to His Life and Work,* Abby Aldrich Rockefeller Fork Art Collection, Williamsburg, Virginia, 1960.

*40. Mrs. H. Weed. *Death of Abel.* (ca. 1830). Embroidery and painting. 28 x 32½". Abby Aldrich Rockefeller Folk Art Collection, Williamsburg, Virginia.

This version of the *Death of Abel,* combining embroidery and painting, is undoubtedly based upon a Biblical illustration or print of the subject. An eighteenth-century book by Salomon Gessner, entitled *The Death of Abel,* was translated into English in 1778 and was widely known. The subject matter also appealed to the Romantics. Byron wrote a *Death of Abel* and Blake drew it intending it to be one of four subjects for a fresco "to ornament the altars of churches to make England like Italy."

Mrs. Weed's interpretation appears closer to the details of Gessner's sentimental elaboration than to the Romantics'. Gessner has Eve cry out: "Oh my son! my son, thy blood rises against me! —it accuses me! unhappy parent! Thus lamented the mother of the human race, while her tears stream'd on the congealing blood. Adam cast on his wife looks full of tenderness and grief: Dear Eve, said he, what exquisite pangs thou giv'st my bursting heart…cease thus reproaching thyself! We both have sinned, we both are guilty… and, stooping to Eve, Adam gently withdrew her feeble hand from the corpse, and pres'd it with ardour to his breast." The two grieving women at the right are the wives of Cain and Abel who (according to Gessner) were named Thirza and Mahala.
Reference: (1) Salomon Gessner, *The Death of Abel,* 3rd ed., London, 1762; (2) Martin Butlin, *William Blake: A Complete Catalogue of the Works in the Tate Gallery,* London, Tate Gallery, 1971.

*41. Artist Unknown. *Adam and Eve.* (ca. 1830). Oil on cardboard. 24¼ x 18½". Whitney Museum of American Art, New York: Gift of Edgar William and Bernice Chrysler Garbisch.

Though weak in draftsmanship, particularly in drawing the human figure, this unknown artist presents the intimacies of a yet-untroubled Eden, in which the wealth and variety of flowers, plants, and trees create a dense and opulent scene. Within this setting, Adam and Eve enjoy an ease with each other and with the animals that is lacking in Erastus Salisbury Field's ordered scene of the Garden of Eden (ill. p.115), where Adam and Eve appear expressionless and somewhat wooden.

42. Artist Unknown. *The Flight into Egypt.* (ca. 1830). Oil on velvet. 19⅝ x 17¼". Collection Edgar William and Bernice Chrysler Garbisch.

Except for the daisy-petaled halo about the child's head, indicating that he is Jesus, the subject of this painting would be difficult to identify. The Christ Child's embroidered or printed gown is the same kind worn by both boys and girls in early nineteenth-century America. The Flight into Egypt was a popular subject in the eighteenth century and the unknown artist must have been familiar with prints or paintings of it, but he has departed freely from traditional representation.

The artist uses a diagrammatic drawing to replace description—i.e., the sun is a face circumscribed by rays, the bulbous contours against the sky indicate hills. The use of signs or symbols to replace naturalistic representations is one of the characteristics of naive art. Another is the intimacy of mood and communication. The family group is portrayed in an accessible and familiar relationship, far from the drama or seriousness of so-called high art.

*43. Ann Johnson. *Baptisam of Our Savour.* (ca. 1840). Watercolor on paper. 19⅞ x 26″. Abby Aldrich Rockefeller Folk Art Collection, Williamsburg, Virginia.

Among the lithographs in the Library of Congress' Division of Photographs and Prints, is John Baker's *Baptism of our Saviour!,* which is certainly Ann Johnson's model for this watercolor. She followed the composition and details more closely than is usual in translations of a composition into another medium by a different hand. However, the color, the simplifications in modeling, and the use of light and shadow give a liveliness to Ann Johnson's version that make it far more interesting than her model.

The *Baptisam* is also interesting as an example of how needlework designs and textures influenced watercolor technique, since we here see watercolor applied in patterns used for needlework stitches. When one looks at the garment of John the Baptist in this painting and compares it with the rendering of the trees and foliage in *The Dead Abel,* this watercolor is closer to the embroidered patterns of the latter than to the textures of the lithograph on which Ann Johnson's *Baptisam* is so obviously based.

*44. John Baker. *The Baptism of Our Saviour!* (copyright 1836). Lithograph. 17-15/16 x 25-5/16". Library of Congress, Washington, D.C.: Prints and Photographs Division.

The Library of Congress attributes this lithograph to John Baker, who signed a companion print on the subject *The Last Supper,* both published by Justin Pierce in 1836. This lithograph is the only example in the exhibition of the kind of popular illustration that made Currier & Ives successful. The New York firm of N. Currier, later Currier & Ives, lithographed 4,300 subjects from 1835 to 1907 for distribution to all the Americas and seaboard Europe, according to Hyatt Mayor. The company produced two standard sizes of prints, both hand-colored by women working in their own homes. Currier & Ives offered for sale "elegant and saleable Pictures—Juvenile, Domestic, Love Scenes, Kittens and Puppies...Catholic Religious, Patriotic... Comic, Family Registers, Memory Pieces and miscellaneous in great Variety."

These popular lithographs of saints and Biblical subjects were so widely distributed that even today they are found in remote areas of northern New Mexico, in patterned tin frames incorporated into altarpieces along with indigenous work. *Reference:* A. Hyatt Mayor, *Prints and People: A Social History of Printed Pictures,* The Metropolitan Museum of Art, New York, 1971.

*45. John Landis. *Jesus in the Upper Room.* 1836. Oil on canvas. 13-9/16 x 18-1/2". Philadelphia Museum of Art: Titus C. Geesey Collection.

This painting is one of several versions by Landis and is more accurately described by a title he used for a much larger one — *Christ and the Apostles Reproving Thomas, the Incredulous Disciple,* the subject being the text "…the doors were shut, but Jesus came and stood among them and said, 'Peace be with you.' Then he said to Thomas, 'Put your finger here, and see my hands; and put out your hand, and place it in my side; do not be faithless, but believing.'"

The larger version was one of ten paintings the eccentric artist offered the Philadelphia Academy of Fine Arts in 1845, after a fire had destroyed many paintings, for the "low price" of $16,000 (the offer was rejected). Others in the list of offered paintings, predominantly religious subjects, were: *Washington at his Devotions with Christ's Ascension, Angel and Women at the Savior's Tomb, The Last Supper, The Stoning of Stephen,* and *St. John.*

Landis proclaimed himself the "anointed of God" and was a self-styled poet and author as well. His history of religious fervour went back to his childhood. His eccentricities of appearance and demeanor were familiar around Harrisburg and the Pennsylvania Academy, where in 1840 someone remarked upon his appearance in "the garb of the fathers of antiquity with hair flowing from his head 18 inches down his breast and a beard of horrific aspect and mammoth magnitude."

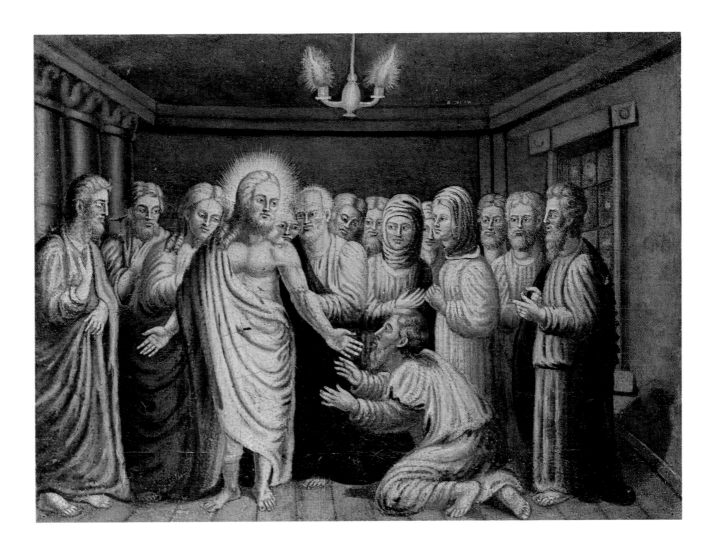

Thomas Cole was the first of the Hudson River School of painters, often characterized as being the first native American school of painting. Though devoted to the study of nature, and usually thought of as a landscape artist, moralistic and religious themes were central to Cole's paintings.

Cole was born in Lancashire, England, and at the age of seventeen, he arrived with his family in Philadelphia. He worked as a commercial engraver at first, but by about 1823–1824 he had determined to become an artist. In 1825 he sold three landscape paintings and that summer he took his first sketching trip up the Hudson River. In 1826 he was elected to the National Academy of Design. In 1829 he went to England and exhibited there, then to France, and in 1831–1832 he lived and toured in Italy. In Rome he occupied the studio of Claude Lorrain, the famous seventeenth-century French artist, whom Cole considered "the greatest of all landscape painters." In 1836 he returned to America and married Maria Bartow of Catskill, where he then set up his studio and residence. In 1841–1842 he made a second trip abroad to London, Paris, Rome, and Sicily. In 1842 he joined the Anglican Church. His first pupil, in 1844, was the landscape artist, Frederic E. Church.

Like Allston and Ryder, Cole wrote poetry. He also kept a journal and wrote lengthy letters to his wife, friends, and patrons. Thus an intimate record of the viewpoint and activities of this gentle, pious, articulate and reflective man is available through Louis Noble's books. A journal entry for May 31, 1835, reads, in part:

> I did not go to church today...I read a little, wrote, and walked, and looked at the landscape...The south wind blew strongly, and dark masses of cloud moved across the twilight sky, the heralds of approaching storm. A leaden hue overspread the vale, the woods, and the distant mountains. How contagious is gloom! A flow of melancholy thoughts and feelings overwhelmed me for a time. I thought of the uncertainty of life; its bootless toil and brevity. The south wind, I thought, would still continue to blow, and bring up its dark clouds for ages after my works, and all the reputation I might gain had faded away, and become as though they had never been,—swept by the wing of time into oblivion's gulf. And shall it be? Shall the spirit, that mysterious principle, unknown even to itself, that vivifies this earth, and generates these thoughts, sink also into the gloomy gulf of non-existence, nor feel again created Beauty, nor see the Nature that it loved so much? It cannot be. The Great Originator, the Mighty One, the Unspeakable, hath not created for purposes vain and useless this power of conceiving,—this wish and "longing after immortality,"—this hope,—this faith which gives an energy to virtue, and raises in the breast these lofty aspirations,—this fear of sinning, of deception and delusion. No! There are no fallacies with God. To prove that, if not to disprove all existence, would be to render all things doubtful.

Reference: (1) Howard S. Merritt, *Thomas Cole*, Memorial Art Gallery, University of Rochester, 1969; (2) Louis L. Noble, *The Life and Works of Thomas Cole*, New York, 1853.

46. Thomas Cole. *St. John the Baptist Preaching in the Wilderness.* 1827. Oil on canvas. 36-3/16 x 29". Wadsworth Atheneum, Hartford, Connecticut: Bequest of Daniel Wadsworth.

This painting, together with *The Expulsion*, its lost pendant *The Garden of Eden,* and the *Moses on the Mount* (owned by the Shelburne Museum) were Cole's earliest efforts at what he called "a higher style of landscape." In this group of early landscapes with religious subject matter, nature appears vast, animated by the sweeping movement of towering clouds, while the figures are tiny. Even the last of the prophets, John the Baptist, and Moses, the greatest of the prophets, are reduced in these canvases to gesticulating pigmy-like figures, whose mighty words and acts are belittled by the expanses of mountainous setting.

*47. Thomas Cole. *The Dead Abel.* (1832). Oil on paper mounted on wood panel. 17⅝ x 28⅞". Albany Institute of History and Art, Albany, New York.

In 1828 Cole exhibited *The Garden of Eden* (now lost) and *The Expulsion from the Garden* at the National Academy of Design. Cole self-consciously considered these paintings examples of "a higher style of landscape." Like the *St. John Preaching in the Wilderness,* these paintings depict nature in awesome and limitless dimensions, with tiny human figures subordinated to it. From 1825 on Cole traveled up the Hudson and into the Catskills, sketching, and in 1827 he went on a sketching trip to the White Mountains. The three paintings mentioned here reflect his experience of nature.

While *The Dead Abel* of 1832 shows that Cole continued to work with Biblical themes, the impact of European study (he spent 1831–1832 in Italy, mainly in Florence) changed his style, particularly in regard to the human figure. He wrote to William Dunlap that *The Dead Abel,* painted at the Academy in Florence, "was intended as a study for a large picture to represent Adam and Eve finding the body of Abel." The larger painting was never done, but *The Dead Abel* remains Cole's most careful figure study and his one painting in which the scale of the figure dominates the natural setting.

*48. Thomas Cole. *The Tempter.* (1843). Oil on canvas. 51 x 40″.
The Baltimore Museum of Art. [Berkeley and Washington
showings only.]

*49. Thomas Cole. *Angels Ministering to Christ in the Wilderness.* 1843. Oil on canvas. 73¾ x 59½". Worcester Art Museum, Worcester, Massachusetts: Charlotte E. W. Buffington Fund.

On July 30, 1843, Thomas Cole noted in his journal: "I am now engaged on a large picture that I trust will be of more importance than anything I have done for a great length of time—It is a scriptural subject—The Angels Ministering to Christ after the Temptation & Fasting—I have painted it in a serious spirit & I trust its effect will be such on the minds of those who see it—I have found great difficulties in consequence of not having suitable models."

The subject of the painting is taken from Matthew 4:11: "Then the devil leaveth him, and, behold, angels came and ministered unto him."

Louis Noble, who was Cole's friend, biographer, and the pastor who received him into the Anglican Church described the painting and how it came to be divided:

> …in from the foreground, the picture widened almost to the boundless [and] had great grandeur, great solemnity, great repose. So predominant were these qualities that the group of celestial figures were thereby thrown into the false position of accessories. To redeem them from that, and give them their due importance, Cole was persuaded by an officious friend to cut the canvass [sic] down to its present size; in which, indeed, there is visible all the subtle, spiritual beauty of the silent, solemn hour represented, but with a sad diminution of its original grandeur as a landscape.

Both parts had remained in the Cole house in Catskill, New York, which continued in the possession of the family. Now belonging to two different museums, the painting is brought together again in this exhibition.

Reference: (1) Manuscript Journal, New York State Library, Albany; (2) Louisa Dresser, "A Scriptural Subject by Thomas Cole: Two Sections Reunited," *Worcester Art Museum News Bulletin* (February, 1971); (3) William H. Gerdts, Jr., *The Baltimore Museum of Art, Annual II,* Baltimore, 1967.

*50. Thomas Cole. *The Guardian Angel.* Oil on canvas. 10¾ x 8½". Collection John Bransten, San Francisco.

This oil sketch for the Guardian Angel who guides and watches over the progress of man from youth to old age is a study for one of Thomas Cole's series, *The Voyage of Life.* The series, of which there are several versions, consists in each case of four paintings. In the first painting the Guardian Angel is seen steering the boat bearing the infant voyager. The present sketch is for the second painting in the series, in which the child, now a youth alone in the boat, takes the helm himself. In Cole's words, now "the Guardian Spirit stands upon the bank of the stream, and with serious yet benignant countenance seems to be bidding the impetuous voyager 'God Speed.'"

The moralistic and theological parable was pointed up by Cole in descriptions he prepared to accompany the paintings. The third painting shows the now middle-aged voyager standing helpless in a rudderless boat in water rushing "furiously down a dark ravine, whirling and foaming" in its wild descent, while the Guardian Angel looks on from the heavens. In the last painting of the series, the Voyager, now an old man, has reached the ocean, and the angels are seen descending the cloudy steps, as if to welcome him to the Haven of Immortal Life.

Cole's deliberate execution of several versions of the series indicates his serious effort to make available to the public, even through engravings and lithographs, subject matter in which artistic excellence served as the bearer of moral and religious meanings. For Cole, art became a parable of sermonic intent.

51. Thomas Cole. *The Good Shepherd.* (Copyright 1849). Lithograph. 11-7/16 x 16-7/16". Library of Congress, Washington, D.C.: Prints and Photographs Division.

The last painting completed by Cole was *The Good Shepherd,* a subject he also drew on a lithograph stone not long before he died. The lithograph in this exhibition belongs to the edition printed "in tint" by Sarony and Major, and published in New York. Cole's widow added the dedicatory inscription beneath the title. In an advertisement for *The Good Shepherd,* the *Record of the Western Art-Union* referred to Cole as a master of Christian art and spoke of Cole's belief "that works of purity and excellence must be cheapened and multiplied in a way to reach every class in the community." Had Cole lived longer, it is likely that he would have used lithography to reach a wider public, to achieve his aim to "unite artistic excellence with subjects of high moral and religious character."
Reference: Howard S. Merritt, *Thomas Cole,* University of Rochester, 1969.

52. Thomas Cole. *A Pilgrim of the Cross at the End of His Journey.* (ca. 1847). Oil on panel. 12 x 18″. National Collection of Fine Arts, Smithsonian Institution, Washington, D.C.

In his later years Cole projected several series of paintings dealing with moral and religious subjects: *The Cross and the World* series, for which this preliminary oil sketch was made; three other series: *Sowing and Reaping,* the *Course of Sacred Empire,* and a series of *Life, Death and Immortality.*

The large painting, for which the painting in this exhibition is a study, was described in the catalogue of the American Art-Union Memorial, 1848, as follows:

> The pilgrim, now an old man on the verge of existence, catches a first view of the boundless and eternal. The tempests of life are behind him; the world is beneath his feet. Its rocky pinnacles, just rising through the gloom, reach not up into his brightness; its sudden mists, pausing in the dark obscurity, ascend no more into his serene atmosphere. He looks out upon the infinite. Clouds—embodiments of glory, threading immensity in countless lines, rolling up from everlasting depths—carry the vision forward toward the unapproachable light. The Cross, now fully revealed, pours its effulgence over the illimitable scene. Angels from the presence, with palm and crown of immortality, appear in the distance, and advance to meet him. Lost in rapture at the sight, the Pilgrim drops his staff, and with uplifted hands sinks upon his knees.

Reference: Howard S. Merritt, *Thomas Cole,* University of Rochester, 1969.

A self-taught artist who spent most of his life in rural Massachusetts, Erastus Salisbury Field, like many of the so-called naive artists, was almost unknown until the 1930s and 1940s. In 1932 The Museum of Modern Art mounted an exhibition *American Folk Art, The Art of the Common Man in America,* and included two portraits by Field. Field's descendants had carefully preserved all the works that remained in their hands, and had made them available to the director of the Springfield Museum. Recognition of their charm and quality followed. Gradually some of the facts of Field's life were pieced together and many of his unsigned paintings were identified.

From 1824 to 1845 Field painted many portraits, some of which are extraordinarily fine, with bold stylizations and remarkable sense of decorative pattern. At the age of nineteen he went to New York and briefly worked in the studio of Samuel F. B. Morse, the artist-inventor who at the time was a successful portrait painter. Field returned to Massachusetts when Morse's young wife died. In 1857 he and his family became members of the second Congregational Church in Palmer, Massachusetts, and except for a period in the 1840s, when he returned to New York and lived in Greenwich Village, he spent the rest of his life in rural Massachusetts.

When the daguerrotype and photography came into use, portrait commissions dwindled. In his later years Field turned to religious and historical paintings, such as those represented here. The sources for these compositions are known in many cases. Perspective and architecture are often based on English paintings by John Martin and Richard Westall and they were mediated through prints; illustrated Bibles provided other elements. In his immense painting, *The Historical Monument of the American Republic,* the various sources, the expository and didactic explanation by the artist, and the sermon inscribed gratuitously across the architecture in the painting become part of Field's grand and wondrous vision, and a masterpiece of American art.

Reference: Mary C. Black, *Erastus Salisbury Field: A Special Exhibition Devoted to His Life and Work,* Abby Aldrich Rockefeller Folk Art Collection, Williamsburg, Virginia, 1963.

*53. Erastus Salisbury Field. *The Garden of Eden.* (ca. 1860–1870). Oil on canvas. 35 x 46″. Museum of Fine Arts, Boston: Gift of Maxim Karolik.

Although Field borrowed from at least three known Biblical illustrations and prints to create this composition, it is nonetheless uniquely his own. Until the painting was restored in this century, Eve and the serpent had been concealed under an additional layer of paint. Whether Field obliterated his own figures or whether someone else did is not known.

Field portrays a tranquil, almost inert Eden in the last moments before Eve's disobedience. Eve is a remarkably innocent and unerotic-looking female. Only the slinking serpent has a sensuous vitality.

54. Erastus Salisbury Field. *"He Turned their Waters into Blood."* (ca. 1865–1880). Oil on canvas. 30¼ x 40½″. National Gallery of Art, Washington, D.C.: Gift of Edgar William and Bernice Chrysler Garbisch, 1964.

55. Erastus Salisbury Field. *The Death of the First Born.* (ca. 1870). Oil on canvas. 35 x 46″. The Metropolitan Museum of Art, New York: Gift of Edgar William and Bernice Chrysler Garbisch, 1966.

56. Erastus Salisbury Field. *Burial of the First Born of Egypt.* (ca. 1880). Oil on canvas. 33¼ x 39¼″. Museum of Fine Arts, Springfield, Massachusetts.

57. Erastus Salisbury Field. *Pharaoh's Army Marching.* (ca. 1865–1880). Oil on canvas. 35 x 46⅛″. Collection Edgar William and Bernice Chrysler Garbisch.

*58. Erastus Salisbury Field. *Israelites Crossing the Red Sea.* (ca. 1865–1880). Oil on canvas. 34¾ x 46". Collection Mr. and Mrs. W. B. Carnochan, Atherton, California.

This cycle of paintings, dealing with the plagues visited upon the Egyptians and the final freeing of the Israelites, was executed by Erastus Salisbury Field between 1865 and 1880. The cycle is based upon prints of paintings by the English artists, John Martin and Richard Westall. But the English artists' romantic expanses of nature and architecture, which provide a theater for the Biblical events, are contracted and reduced by Field. He transforms the Egyptian architecture into what seems like operatic stage sets, and rather shaky ones at that. Yet the Egyptoid columns which seem to float on their bases, and overlap the pediments they are supposed to support, play a powerful expressive role. In *Burial of the First Born,* the reiterated vertical thrusts of the large columns give a special pathos to the tiny vertical figures of the mourning parents bearing the white-shrouded burdens of their dead infants. Similarly, in *Pharaoh's Army Marching,* the columns provide a deep, resonant, throbbing beat as a counterpoint to the more staccato rhythm of the repeated verticals of the helmeted officers in their relentless forward movement. Most curious of all is the painting of the *Israelites Crossing the Red Sea*—the waters follow the description in the Bible and are indeed "a wall unto them on their right hand, and on their left." In the first ranks, moving toward the spectator are the "mixed multitude" of "flocks, and herds and even very much cattle." Behind are the six hundred thousand children of Israel on foot, and behind them is the pillar of fire which, when the Egyptians pursued, moved from before them to behind them (Exodus 14:19,22). But Field illustrates the Biblical text with fidelity. The masses move toward the new land beneath a star-pricked nighttime sky. Within the forward group are several spectral figures of immense size, perhaps showing that the artist at some point changed the scale of the figures.

In Erastus Salisbury Field's series on *Plagues of Egypt* and the *Crossing of the Red Sea,* Moses, to whom all of the directives were given by the Lord, is notably absent. Only in the plague when *He Turned Their Waters into Blood* is Moses seen at the far right standing with Aaron on the steps, a tiny figure with hands out, palms upward, looking into the darkened skies. Could the figure in the *Death of the First Born* who is seated at the lower right, be Moses, also? He sits looking up, his face intent and grim, on the steps leading to the place where Pharaoh and his grieving family are: it was this last punishment which led Pharaoh to call Moses and direct him to take the people of Israel and their flocks and go.

*59. Erastus Salisbury Field. *Historical Monument of the American Republic.* (1876). Photo engraving. 15 x 22¾". Museum of Fine Arts, Springfield, Massachusetts: Loaned by Miss Pauline Williams.

Erastus Field's masterpiece was an enormous painting, done in commemoration of the hundredth anniversary of American independence. Because of its size, the painting is now permanently installed at the Springfield Museum. An engraving of it was made by E. Bierstadt in 1876, the same year of the painting and presumably at the instigation of Field. A print of the engraving is exhibited here.

The *Monument* is extraordinary both as a work of art and as a document. Some of the sources for the composition have been identified by Mary Black. They range from a Biblical illustration of the Tower of Babel through works by Cole, West, Trumbull, and the English artist, John Martin. But all the motifs and data taken from other artists are welded together in an awesome vision, a superstructure decorated with sculpture which give events of American history as Field interpreted it, including a plea for the cause of Abolition. Field wrote a descriptive catalogue and explained the monument, beginning with some *Remarks:*

> A professed architect, on looking at this picture, might have the impression that a structure built in this form would not stand...I am not a professed architect, and some things about it may be faulty. Be that as it may, my aim has been to get up a brief history of our country or epitome, in a monumental form...The figures and emblems are represented to be raised work or bass-relief [sic], with the exception of a portion of the figures, which are statues. The dark figures are represented in bronze to denote the colored race. The architecture varies, to accord more or less with the subject or sentiment.

Following the *Remarks* are *Descriptions* identifying the episodes numbered on the towers. Near the top of each tower are the letters T.T.B., "The True Base." Standing on The True Base are columns symbolizing the States then in the Union. The columns "are mounted by the goddess of Liberty, and angels stand between them with the crowns. The columns are partly encompassed. The Towers are connected with suspension bridges, and cars are going to and fro from the centennial ex-

hibition, which is on the top of the central tower. The troops are marching around the monument which illustrates the centennial anniversary of the American Independence."

Field's *Description* makes it clear that his religious viewpoint colors and informs his understanding of American history. For example, he represents angels denoting divine providence interfering on behalf of the slaves. But a more explicitly religious didacticism is to be seen in an essay on the Bible, which is carved into the building at the lower left. Not all of the essay in the original painting is reproduced in the engraving; excerpts from the complete text read:

> THE BIBLE is a brief recital of all that is past and a certain prediction of all that is to come...It reveals the only living and true God, and points the unerring way to Him...THE BIBLE is a book of...wisdom which condemns all foolishness and vice...It is a book of truth that detects all lies, and confutes all error; and a book of life; which leads in the sure way from eternal death. THE BIBLE is the most compendious work in the world...It contains the earliest antiquities, the strangest events, the most wonderful occurrences, heroic deeds, and unparalleled wars; it describes the celestial, terrestrial, and infernal worlds; the origin of the angelic host, the human tribes, and hellish legions... This book is the kings best copy, the magistrate's best rule, the parent's best guide, the servant's infallible directory, and the young man's best companion. It is the schoolboy's spelling book, and the learned man's masterpiece. It contains a choice grammer for the novice, and deep sayings for the sage...Inexcusable is he who does not read, and unwise is he who gains no instruction; for to guilty man it is a savor of life unto life, or of death unto death.

Reference: Mary C. Black, *Erastus Salisbury Field: A Special Exhibition Devoted to His Life and Work,* Abby Aldrich Rockefeller Folk Art Collection, Williamsburg, Virginia, 1963.

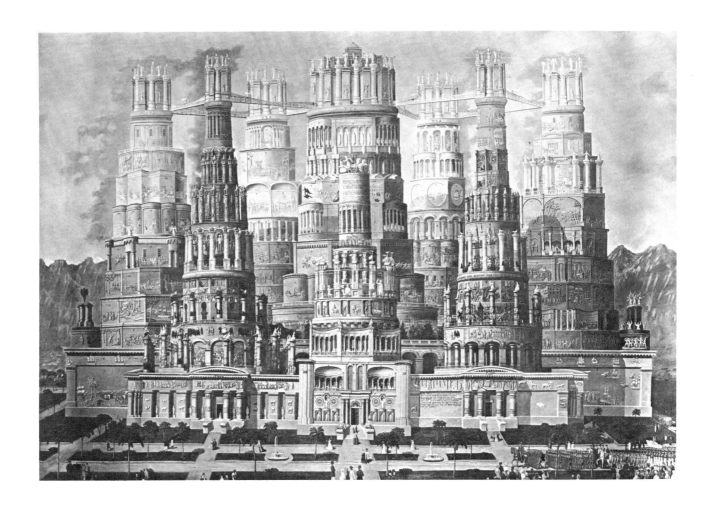

Carl Christian Anton Christensen (1831–1912)

60. Carl Christian Anton Christensen. *A Panorama of Mormon History:* seven episodes from a total of twenty-two: (1) *Moroni's Appearance to Joseph Smith;* (2) *Death of Joseph Smith;* (3) *The Assassins and the Body of Joseph Smith;* (15) *The Nauvoo Temple;* (16) *Burning of the Nauvoo Temple;* (17) *Crossing the Ice, The Trek out of Nauvoo;* (19) *The Descent of the Thousands of Quail.* (1869–1890). Oil on linen. 96 x 120″, each episode. Brigham Young University Art Collection, Provo, Utah. [Berkeley showing only.]

New Mexican altar panel paintings *(retablos)* and free-standing carved figures *(bultos)*, generally referred to as *santos*, form a quite distinctive entity in nineteenth-century art. They form the largest and most cohesive group of extant, indigenous paintings and sculptures which were created under the aegis of the Roman Catholic church. They are also the most isolated. E. Boyd, who has spent a lifetime in reconstructing the history and recovering the corpus of New Mexican art has written of the santos:

> Santos...made in colonial New Mexico are strikingly different in their materials, intensity of feeling, and lack of theatrical affectation from contemporary images made in other Spanish colonies such as New Spain, New Granada, and Peru. This apparent originality grew out of geographic and cultural isolation, a condition almost forgotten today...

The traditional iconography of the santos was mediated by indigenous Mexican art based on Spanish prototypes. But the motifs are freely adapted. New saints with new attributes appear side by side with the traditional images deriving from paintings of Murillo, Zurbaran, and Velasquez that had centuries of orthodoxy behind them. The New Mexican panels and carvings can be distinguished from Mexican examples: they are more linear and decorative; they appear flat, with little indication of perspective or atmospheric space. They communicate an intense sense of the spiritual realities that they diagram, but do not describe.

The historical development of New Mexican art helps inform an understanding of its place and function. In 1540 several entries into the present southwestern United States were made overland by settlers from Mexico City. They ranged from Baja California to what is now Kansas. Despite overwhelming odds —settlers were entirely self-dependent in providing tools, arms, food, clothing, and defense from hostile Indians—the Kingdom of New Mexico grew until it extended from the Rio Grande valley into mountain valleys 300 miles north and south of the river, and 100 miles east and west. The colonists brought with them or made their religious artifacts and whatever else they needed; communication with New Spain was infrequent, unreliable, and supplies to the missions of any sort, from writing paper to holy oils, were scanty. What paintings and sculptures may have come in 1598 with settlers to New Mexico were destroyed in the uprising in 1680 of the Pueblo Indians.

The colonial population increased and prospered despite all reverses. To supplement the scanty liturgical ornaments that continued to trickle in from New Spain, the *santeros,* the makers of holy objects, carved bultos from pine or seasoned cottonwood root, making the figures in sections with ax, adz and knife, and smoothing them with sandstone. The figures were doweled together, then covered with a thin layer of gesso made from native gypsum by the Italian gesso formula that was taken with the padres to the New World; cloth was sometimes dipped in the gesso, draped on the figure and allowed to harden, and then painted with details of clothing and drapery. The retablos were done on hand-adzed pine panels, for the most part, and were sized with gesso before being painted.

By the late nineteenth century, commercial religious goods finally reached New Mexico in some quantity, with a consequent decline in the demand for santos as well as in the quality of those produced. Boyd notes that the exception to this decline was found in the market provided the santeros by the *confraternites,* brotherhoods of Penitentes, that needed to furnish their chapter-houses, called *moradas,* with images. These religious associations for laymen and -women, in which membership was a matter of course, survived from earliest colonial days, outgrowths of the Third Order of St. Francis. Their social functions became very important in the community and competition among chapters was sometimes intense. Members commissioned and furbished their own chapter's santos, and carried the resplendent images through the streets on saints' feast-days. Boyd relates that "the principal figures of the Passion were required for each morada: The Nazarene Christ, a Crucifix, often jointed to allow removal from the cross on Good Friday for placement in a sepulchre; an image of Our Lady of Sorrows; and often one of St. John the Disciple. Many small crucifixes and crosses were also required. These subjects continued to employ later santeros."

Most of the retablos and bultos in this exhibition were originally incorporated into large altar-pieces composed of many panels and recessed areas into which the carved bultos were placed, as in niches.

Reference: E. Boyd, *The New Mexican Santero,* Santa Fe, 1969.

*61. José Aragón. *St. Michael the Archangel.* Tempera over gesso on hand-adzed pine. 27-15/16 x 15-3/4". Museum of New Mexico, Santa Fe.

José Aragón's descendants report that he was born in Spain and came to New Mexico in 1820. Tree-ring tests on his panels confirm his recorded stay between 1820 and 1837. Some of Aragón's panels bear long prayers; some are signed and dated. He occasionally referred to his sculpture shop and used the prefix "don" before his name. His many *reredos* show some influences from engravings, but are regional in style.

Aragón's St. Michael, shown in his role of dragon-slaying warrior, is delineated by curving springing lines, some bold and others fine. The wings, small in relationship to his body, are emphasized by heavy outlines. The line making the continuous contour of brows, bridge of nose, and nostril, creates a design of great delicacy.

The quality of the line changes in the amusing dragon. His features are ponderous, their heaviness offset by the randomly incised looped hooks along his flattened body, which form patterns that repeat the flourish of the tail recurved upon itself.

62. Pedro Fresquis. *Our Lady of Guadalupe.* (ca. 1810–1820). Tempera on gessoed pine. 28 x 14″. The Taylor Museum of the Colorado Springs Fine Arts Center.

Pedro Antonio Fresquis, the first New Mexican-born santero, was a direct descendant of a Flemish miner whose family settled in Santa Cruz where Pedro Antonio was born in 1749. Over his long lifetime Fresquis made altarscreens for the Rosario Chapel at Santa Fe, and for chapels at Nambé Pueblo, Las Truchas, and Chamita, New Mexico. E. Boyd notes that his work is characterized by a sense of space-filling by improvised motifs, and also by the habit of incising through the painted surface into the gesso.

Our Lady of Guadalupe was one of the most frequently represented images. Three versions are in this exhibition. All are modeled after the picture now in the basilica of Guadalupe in Mexico City, said to have been miraculously painted on the garment of the Indian, Juan Diego, to whom the Virgin appeared four times in 1531.

63. José Aragón. *Our Lady of Guadalupe.* Tempera on pine panel. 24-13/16 x 20-7/8″. Museum of New Mexico, Santa Fe.

In the four roundels of this reredos panel are scenes of the miraculous appearance of Our Lady of Guadalupe to the Indian, Juan Diego (see preceding entry).

64. Artist Unknown. *Our Lady of Guadalupe.* (ca. 1835). Tempera on pine. 24″ high. Museum of New Mexico, Santa Fe.

***65.** José Aragón. *The Holy Trinity.* Tempera on pine panel. 16⅛ x 12″. Museum of New Mexico, Santa Fe.

The New Mexican santeros' representations of the Trinity reflect the persistence of an ancient type—three identical human figures seated side-by-side. Byzantine art used this imagery, but subsequent periods created every possible variation on the theme—one body with three heads, and also one body and one neck with three faces. The theme in all its variations was proscribed in 1745 by Pope Benedict XIV. This did not prevent the artists of Mexico and New Mexico from continuing their three-figure representations. Each of the three points to their individual symbolization at their breasts—the lamb for Christ, the sun for God, the dove for the Holy Spirit. The round object beneath them is the world. The center figure, God the Father, is usually distinguished in some manner from the other two—in this case his head is positioned slightly higher than the flanking figures.

66. José Aragón. *The Trinity ("Trinidad").* (ca. 1825–1830). Tempera on gessoed pine. 18 x 13½". The Taylor Museum of the Colorado Springs Fine Arts Center.

***67.** José Aragón. *Holy Family.* (ca. 1820–1825). Tempera on gessoed pine. 21 x 16". The Taylor Museum of the Colorado Springs Fine Arts Center.

This charming panel reads in two dimensions: the horizontal plane shows the sturdy child Jesus firmly held by his parents on either side, Joseph with his attribute, a flowering branch, in one hand, and Mary coiffed as a nun. The vertical plane shows God the Father above with a gesture that commands the scene below; then the dove of the Holy Spirit, hovering above the head of Jesus, who completes the Holy Trinity. The diagrammatic aspect of the composition is intentional; it forms a cross with the dove at its intersection.

*68. José Aragón. *Crucifixion.* (ca. 1825). Tempera on gessoed pine. 19 x 11″. The Taylor Museum of the Colorado Springs Fine Arts Center.

This Crucifixion is not an attempt to portray an historical event, but seems to be a depiction of devotional and liturgical images, which could account for the icon-like quality of the panel. One would be justified in supposing that Aragón's source was the type of sculptured Crucifix and carved bulto found even today in New Mexican churches. The figure of Christ is larger than the two attending figures, as is the case in actual altar carvings. The attendants of this panel are Our Lady of Sorrows and St. John. The chandeliers are like those found in the chancels of New Mexico churches, and the vertical branches with which Aragón has filled the spaces between the figures are also standard elements of church decoration that are often carved or made of patterned tin.

The loincloth about Christ, with its great projecting bow, usually on His left side, is also typical of this kind of altar Crucifix and derives from Mexican Spanish-Colonial examples.

69. Artist Unknown. *Crucifix.* Wood. 56 x 43 x 7″. Collection Mr. and Mrs. Nathan Oliveira, Palo Alto, California. [Berkeley showing only.]

70. Artist Unknown. *Crucifix.* Polychromed wood. 30 x 20″. Collection Mr. and Mrs. W. B. Carnochan, Atherton, California. [Berkeley showing only.]

71. Artist Unknown. *Crucifix with Cupbearing Angel.* (late 19th century). Oil on cottonwood root. 31-1/16 x 15-3/8″. Museum of New Mexico, Santa Fe: Spanish Colonial Arts Society Collections.

The little angel holding a chalice to receive the blood from the wound in Christ's side is another ancient motif adapted to the style and imagery of the New Mexican santeros. The motif of angels fluttering about the hands, the feet and side of Christ receiving the blood in chalices was introduced into European painting during the Renaissance. Some of the Crucifixes made by the santeros have a cavity at the back of the corpus covered only by quills which represent ribs; within the cavity is suspended a heart. The identification with the suffering of Christ at the time of the Passion was expressed by the artist, to be re-experienced by the viewer through these vivid reminders of His physical suffering.

72. José Aragón. *Our Lady of the Wayfarers.* (ca. 1820–1825). Tempera on gessoed pine. 20½ x 16″. The Taylor Museum of the Colorado Springs Fine Arts Center.

In this advocation the New Mexican artist represents the Virgin as frontal, hieratical, and symmetrical. This type goes back to a form of Byzantine and medieval representation wherein the Virgin holds the Child over her womb. The variety, vigor, and whimsy of the decoration does not detract from the solemnity of the crowned Mother and Child. As in the eastern and medieval prototypes, the infant Christ is not child-like, but has the majestic bearing of one who rules. The bell-shape of her head and gown is repeated in the crowned infant Christ.

Juan Ramon Velasquez (1820–1902)

Artist Unknown

José Aragón

73. Juan Ramon Velasquez. *Crucifix.* (post-1880). Oil on pine. 58¼ x 39″. Museum of New Mexico, Santa Fe.

"Juan Ramon Velasquez was an outstanding maker of the late class of bulto for the vast region in northern New Mexico where he lived...Born during the 1820s, Velasquez died in 1902 ...In his later years he made bultos for many moradas, often very large ones...

"Velasquez was the only bulto maker to solve successfully a structural problem in making the corpus of a crucifix. Instead of assembling small pieces of wood to form the legs and feet of a corpus, which inevitably came apart in the course of time, he took the time and trouble to carve the entire legs and feet from a single log of pine.

"His earlier bultos were painted with the usual local water soluble colors, but after oil house paints were carried in general stores, he used these. Such figures have no other layer of painting on them and these are his original colors."
Reference: E. Boyd, *The New Mexico Santero,* Santa Fe, 1969.

74. Artist Unknown. *Our Lady.* Polychromed wood. 18″ high. Collection Mr. and Mrs. W. B. Carnochan, Atherton, California. [Berkeley showing only.]

75. José Aragón. *Our Lady of the Rosary.* (ca. 1825–1830). Tempera on gessoed pine. 26¼ x 16¼″. The Taylor Museum of the Colorado Springs Fine Arts Center.

In this advocation the Virgin holds a rosary in one hand; often St. Dominic is present receiving the rosary. She is crowned as queen of heaven, and holds the Christ Child in one arm. Beneath her feet is the crescent moon, a symbol deriving from the Book of Revelation. The subject matter has a long history in European art, especially after Caravaggio's famous painting of the subject. The flat, decorative elaboration of the Virgin's gown, and the solemn unfocused gaze of her eyes give an icon-like quality to the panel.

76. José Aragón. *Our Lady of Carmen.* (ca. 1825). Tempera on gessoed pine. 27½ x 14¼″. The Taylor Museum of the Colorado Springs Fine Arts Center.

This advocation of the Virgin is usually distinguished by a brown flowered robe or a red robe with a yellow panel; she is crowned and holds the Christ Child and a scapular bearing the emblem of her Confraternity. She is the intercessor for souls in Purgatory: these are seen below, bust-length nude figures, two chained together and all with their hands in the attitude of prayer.

77. Artist Unknown. *The Good Shepherdess.* (late 19th century). Tempera on gesso on pine. 15¾″ high. Museum of New Mexico, Santa Fe.

Traditional iconography in Christian art includes the figure of the Good Shepherd, which represents the parable and is also an image of Christ, dating from the time of the catacombs. But the Good Shepherdess, another of the advocations of the Virgin Mary, is also encountered in New Mexican art of the nineteenth century.

78. Rafael Aragón. *St. Raymond ("San Ramon Nonato").* (ca. 1850). Tempera on gessoed pine. 23¾ x 17″. The Taylor Museum of the Colorado Springs Fine Arts Center.

San Ramon Nonato, born by Caesarian section, was patron saint of midwives and was especially revered by expectant mothers. He is shown wearing a chasuble and holding a monstrance and a wand bearing three crowns, symbols of the earthly honors that he rejected. He spent his life ransoming Christians from Moorish Africa.

José Rafael Aragón of Córdova, New Mexico, was exceedingly productive. (Apparently he was not related to the earlier José Aragón; to avoid confusion he is referred to by his second name.) His earliest large altarscreen was completed before 1826. By that time his own style, distinguished by positive outlines and clear areas of color, was developed. He did altarscreens for the Durán chapel, the famous Santuario de Chimayo, for a chapel at Córdova, and for many other chapels in northern New Mexico. The uneven quality of his work may reflect the hands of the many helpers he apparently had to accomplish all that he did.

79. Artist Unknown. *The Archangel Raphael.* Tempera (?) on wood. 18 x 10″. Collection Mr. and Mrs. W. B. Carnochan, Atherton, California. [Berkeley showing only].

The archangel Raphael appeared to Tobias and healed his father's blindness by telling him to catch a fish, burn it, and anoint his father's eyes with the ashes which, if he had faith, would cure the blindness. Since the archangel had guided Tobias, and was thought also to be the angel who appeared to the Shepherds to announce the birth of Christ, Raphael came to be regarded as a guardian spirit or guardian angel of humanity. In New Mexican art he is usually represented with a pilgrim's tunic, staff, and gourd for water. He also carries a fish, referring of course to the Tobias story.

80. Jose Benito Ortega. *The Archangel Raphael.* Tempera on cottonwood. 16⅛″ high. Museum of New Mexico, Santa Fe.

81. Artist Unknown. *St. Barbara.* (ca. 1830–1850). Tempera on pine. 22-1/16″ high. Museum of New Mexico, Santa Fe.

St. Barbara was an early Christian martyr whom the New Mexican santeros represented wearing a three-tiered skirt, plumed crown, and holding a palm, symbol of martyrdom. In panel paintings the tower in which she was imprisoned is also usually represented.

82. Rafael Aragón. *St. Christopher.* Tempera on pine panel. 12⅝ x 9⅞″. Museum of New Mexico, Santa Fe.

St. Christopher, the patron of travelers, is usually shown as a barelegged giant bearing the Christ Child across a river. The ancient legend tells that Christopher used his great strength to help carry wayfarers across a river: by night a child came and asked to be taken across but as they went the child became increasingly heavy until Christopher felt the whole world could not be more of a burden; at the other side, the child said to Christopher, "Thou hast not only borne the world, but him who made the world upon thy shoulders." The orb surmounted by a cross held by the Christ Child in this panel symbolizes the world under his rulership.

The word fractur comes from "fraktur," or broken printing. The method was used for illuminated manuscripts in Europe before the invention of printing. It was eventually brought to America by religious refugees from the German Palatinate. At first it was used for devotional purposes only, as by the monks at Ephrata Cloister, a Seventh Day Baptist sect at Ephrata, Pennsylvania. But by 1819 Alice Ford notes that fractures were so popular that Johann Krauss published an art instruction book on the illumination art in Allentown, Pennsylvania.

Fractur paintings vary greatly in subject and purpose, being sometimes certificates of birth, baptism, or confirmation, memorials, house blessings. A group of Ephrata sacred books, noted in Alice Ford's book, which helped set the Pennsylvania Dutch decorative style, are still in existence.

Reference: (1) Alice Ford, *Pictorial Folk Art New England to California,* New York Studio Publications, 1949; (2) Donald A. Shelley, *The Fraktur-Writings or Illuminated Manuscripts of the Pennsylvania Germans,* Allentown, Pennsylvania German Folklore Society, 1961.

*83. The Reverend George Geistweite. *The 34th Psalm.* 1801. Fractur, pen and ink over watercolor on paper. 12½ x 15⅛". Philadelphia Museum of Art: Titus C. Geesey Collection.

"This exquisite example of fraktur—a quotation from the 34th Psalm,—is without a doubt the finest example of an illuminated manuscript made by a folk artist in this country.

"It is the work of the Reverend George Geistweite, a circuit-riding minister of the Reformed Church in Centre County, Pennsylvania, who also taught from 1794 to 1804 in the first school established there. Where the Reverend Geistweite found time in such a strenuous life in a newly developed area to devote himself to creating the minute details so lovingly worked out in line and color is not known, but only a person with the skill and patience of a mediaeval monk could have delineated ornament with such delicacy. The fraktur is only 12½ by 15 inches, yet the narrow inner border, composed of tiny 1/16 inch blocks is painted accurately in four colors. A love of drawing animals and birds caused him to fill all spaces not given over to floral decorations with fauna in various sizes. There are hens and chickens, dogs and lions, unicorns and peacocks. The double-headed eagle and mystical pelican are enclosed in the scrolls which form the great capital letter 'I' which begins the quotation from the psalm: 'I will bless the Lord at all times.'"

Reference: Pennsylvania Dutch Folk Arts, The Philadelphia Museum of Art.

*84. Artist Unknown. *Religious Text—The Crucifixion.* 1847. Watercolor on paper. 13½ x 10¾″. Abby Aldrich Rockefeller Folk Art Collection, Williamsburg, Virginia.

At least two other fracturs exist with the same strangely stylized scene of the Crucifixion in their upper zones. Biblical quotations fill the background about the figures: they read from left to right in the upper zone next to the left thief, "Today you will be with me in Paradise" (Luke 23:43); in the arch about the Crucified Christ, "There they crucified him, and with him two murderers on each side Jesus in the midst" (John 19:18); in the upper right next to the thief, "But one of the evildoers who hanged blasphemed him" (Luke 23:39); second zone, left, "One of the soldiers opened his side with a spear and immediately there came blood and water from it" (John 19:34); center, "They have my garments among themselves divided"; right, "But Jesus said Father forgive them, for they know not what they do, and they have cast over my robe the lots" (John 19:24); beneath the cross, in the border, "Golgotha, that is skull place."

The text in the lower zone repeatedly refers to Jesus' blood: "Jesus' blood come over me. So call I thirstily, Jesus' blood come and be with me, my soul and body, with me, my house and home my heart and mind, come and abide Jesus' blood. I behold you also in faith."

Professor Wilhelm Wuellner, a colleague who knows the pietist historical background out of which these texts come, translated the material and conjectured that two different hymns are quoted, that the writer of the script miscalculated the spacing of the calligraphy and then was forced to change to the current style of handwriting of the last four lines. It is possible that the upper zone and border may predate the calligraphy by some decades. The fractur owned by The Metropolitan Museum of Art, which is similar in the upper zone but has only decorative flowers in the second zone, is clearly dated 1800.

85. Artist Unknown. *Floral Design and Religious Quotation.* 1793. Fractur (made for Christina Beary), pen and ink and watercolor on paper. 15¾ x 12⅞″. Philadelphia Museum of Art: Titus C. Geesey Collection.

This fractur made for Christina Beary has fanciful and decorative birds surrounding a quotation from Psalm 121: "I lift mine eyes unto the hills whence comes to me help from the Lord who made heaven and earth. The Lord keep you from all evil; he keep your soul. The Lord keep your going and coming, now and for ever." Then follows the statement, "Inscribed on the 10th of February 1793."

86. Artist Unknown. *A Present from Mother Ann to Mary H.* 1848. Ink and watercolor on paper. 14 x 14¼″. Abby Aldrich Rockefeller Folk Art Collection, Williamsburg, Virginia.

The mystical awareness of the voice of God, or inner voice, is fundamental to Quaker beliefs. It was thus that Ann Lee, an English Quaker subject to having visions, was directed in one of them to go in 1774 to America, where she established a Shaking Quaker settlement at Watervliet, New York, made a missionary trip through New England, and died ten years afterward, having given impetus and direction to the Shaker sect, whose members were subject to trances and ecstasies.

The most remarkable flowering of what came to be known as Shaker spiritualism occurred in New England in the early nineteenth century. On August 16, 1837, some children showed signs of being entranced and began to whirl and shake. The manifestations spread, the sect refers to this period as "Mother Ann's Second Coming," or "The New Era of Manifestations." In the 1840s the Shakers of Hancock, Massachusetts went ecstatically to "Mount Sinai," the mountain north of the village, to receive bounteous imaginary "gifts" of food, jewels, clothing, including "a flaming trumpet, which the Saviour placed on each of our shoulders," a box of spectacles "that they may see more clearly spiritual things"...and "a box of spiritual guns from George Washington for the brethren."

In time these spiritual gifts were graphically rendered on "Sacred Sheets," like this one, where quotations and admonitions are interspersed among a watch and chain, a tree of life, an elaborate large lamp, a beehive, a table with a decanter of wine and a goblet, a figure in a strange airship with a flag, labeled "Freedom," and an open book with Mother Ann's directives clearly inscribed.

Reference: Andrew Deming Andrews and Faith Andrews, *Vision of the Heavenly Sphere, A Study in Shaker Religious Art,* Charlottesville, University of Virginia Press, 1969.

*87. Artist Unknown (attributed erroneously to Washington Allston). *Paul and Silas in Prison.* (n.d.). Oil on wood. 24 x 30". Washington University Gallery of Art, St. Louis, Missouri.

This strange painting has long been mistakenly attributed to Washington Allston, probably because the initials WA appear in the lower left corner. Additional study of the painting is necessary, but it appears closer to John Quidor (1801–1881) than to Allston. Quidor, one of the most original of American artists, did a series of "gigantic Scriptural paintings" he intended to use as partial payment of a farm in Illinois. None survive, but at least three paintings were completed, exhibited, and recorded; four more were projected.

The painting is unusual in its choice of subject (the *Index of Christian Art* has only one reference to a depiction of the episode, and that in the thirteenth century) and in its uneven execution. Expressive strong passages and figures contrast with careless and inept ones. The painting refers to the imprisonment of Paul and Silas, his amanuensis, at Philippi; the jailer charged with their safekeeping put them in stocks deep in the inner prison.

> . . . at midnight Paul and Silas prayed, and sang praises unto God. . . And suddenly there was a great earthquake, so that the foundations of the prison were shaken: and immediately all doors were opened, and everyone's bands were loosed. And the keeper of the prison awaking out of his sleep, and seeing the prison doors open, he drew out his sword, and would have killed himself, supposing that the prisoners had fled. But Paul cried with a loud voice, saying, 'Do thyself no harm: for we are all here'. Then he called for a light, and sprang in, and came trembling, and fell down before Paul and Silas. (Acts 16: 25–29).

The episode concludes with the conversion of the jailer and his family. The painting portrays the moment at which the jailer asks of Paul what he must do to be saved.

William Rimmer (1816-1879)

During his lifetime Rimmer was shoemaker, granite worker, self-taught physician and surgeon, anatomist, art teacher, public lecturer, and head of art schools in New York and Boston. He was also a painter and sculptor of extraordinary talent, but his known total output was uneven in quality and smaller in quantity than one would assume in a career that spanned more than four decades. His work ranges from a fine sculpture called *Despair,* done in 1830, to sculptures from the 1870s.

Surprisingly, a significant number of his known works have religious subject matter. His biographer, Truman Bartlett, relates that several Catholic priests of the Boston area were his first and, for some time, his most important patrons. His ease with Catholic clergy perhaps stemmed from his family background, which on his father's side may have been French Catholic. His father, according to Bartlett, was spirited out of France at the time of the French Revolution and raised in England, reportedly at the expense of British and Russian monarchies. Encouraged by his supporters in the belief that he was the escaped Dauphin, he fled to North America when another contender ascended the throne of France. But ever afterwards he alternated between hope and despair in regard to what he dreamed to be his rightful legacy. Certainly the son's first sculpture, *Despair,* known to be of his father, and the *Fall of Evening* reflect this background.

William Rimmer married a Quaker and, insisting that his family attend public worship, he rented a pew in whatever church the family wished to attend in their many moves from place to place. He wrote: "Remember! that the faculty of reason is below the faculty of worship; and the Protestants may in striving to admit the mind to the path of duty by the one, draw the soul's attention from the holiest promptings of the other, which the Catholics so much do honor, as the safer master for the conscience."

In his early years he painted a *Virgin, Infant Jesus and Joseph,* an *Infant Saviour,* a *Crucifixion,* and an *Infant St. Peter.* The latter two, reproduced in Bartlett's work, are close to the traditional iconography and style of art for the church. However, the *Coronation of Queen Esther* of 1847 and the *Massacre of the Innocents* from the period when Rimmer lived in East Milton, Massachusetts (1855-1861) emphasize the drama of Biblical events. Rather than being characterized by the traditional devotional and liturgical nature of church art, they depict the Biblical events in dramatic, imaginative recreations of the event, in exotic architectural settings.

Reference: Truman Bartlett, *The Art and Life of William Rimmer, Sculptor, Painter, and Physician,* Boston, 1882.

88. William Rimmer. *Coronation of Queen Esther.* 1847. Oil on panel. 19¾ x 26¼". The Herbert W. Plimpton Collection, Amherst College, Amherst, Massachusetts.

The Book of Esther 2:15–18 relates that Esther was chosen by Ahasuerus to be Queen above Vashti, and that Ahasuerus loved Esther above all other women because of her selflessness and beauty. A Jew herself, Esther was able as queen to intercede with the king on behalf of the many Jews in his kingdom, influencing him to mitigate harsh taxes and tributes.

In the *Coronation of Queen Esther,* Rimmer depicts the panoplied Oriental court of the royal palace with an evocative sensuousness. One is drawn into the story, searching among the onlookers for Hegai, the king's eunuch who had charge of the women, and whose directions Esther scrupulously followed. King Ahasuerus, regal and tall beyond natural proportions, is seen setting the royal crown upon Esther, who had found "grace and favor in his sight more than all the virgins." The Coronation event must have had a special significance to the artist, who had been raised with the tales of his father's expectations of the French crown and of his subsequent disappointment, flight, and despair.

89. William Rimmer. *Massacre of the Innocents.* (n.d.). Oil on canvas. 27 x 22". The Herbert W. Plimpton Collection, Amherst College, Amherst, Massachusetts.

Herod's order that all the infants of Bethlehem be killed to protect him from a prophesied rival is an episode often represented in Continental art, and then most often with large crowds and soldiers advancing upon the helpless mothers who vainly try to protect their infants. Rimmer instead focuses upon one incident that becomes the prototype for the larger event. Rimmer's contemporary and biographer Truman Bartlett interpreted the painting thus:

> The idea that the artist wished to convey seems to have been, that this mother had gone to the top of the temple, where incense to the gods was burning, there placing herself and child under its divinely perfumed and most sacred guardianship with perfect confidence in its protective potency. To find human cruelty triumphant in such a place, and Heaven merciless, overcomes her; and she turns her eyes upward in an agony of protesting, despairing appeal.

Reference: Truman H. Bartlett, *The Art and Life of William Rimmer, Sculptor, Painter, and Physician,* Boston, 1882.

*90. William Rimmer. *God the Father Creating the Sun and Moon.* 1869. Sanguine over pencil on paper. 17¾ x 12¾". Fogg Art Museum, Harvard University, Cambridge, Massachusetts: Louise E. Bettens Fund. [Ill. p.27].

Although this is a small sketch, it evokes a large, even a gigantic image. Rimmer's conception is clearly related to Michelangelo's fresco of the same subject, in which appear two images of God, one at the right moving toward the viewer, and one at the left moving away. Rimmer apparently combined the two Michelangelesque conceptions, using the outspread arms and the back view. The extremely foreshortened over-the-shoulder view of God's extended right index finger recalls the familiar Creation of Adam gesture.

Despite such recollections, Rimmer's God the Creator has its own distinctiveness. The large, muscular torso has the energy and vitality of a Paul Bunyan, rather than the pervasive power of Michelangelo's classically inspired God. There is a strange disparity between the contracted muscles of the back and the relaxed, almost languid repose of the legs. Michelangelo's images are remembered for their concentration of power, while Rimmer's God the Creator, while capturing the eye and imagination, tends to become more diffuse and ambiguous on prolonged viewing.

*91. William Rimmer. *Evening: Fall of Day.* (1869). Oil on canvas. 40 x 50". Museum of Fine Arts, Boston.

This painting might well be called The Fall of Lucifer. The immense figure forms a jagged arc; Rimmer contrasts the intricate ovoid pattern of the carefully delineated strained muscles with the delicate, sinuous lines of the feathers which make up the wondrous wings and the flame-like hair. The great circular halo about the head, the star which is illumined against the dark underside of one wing, the foot which touches the horizon but is not supported by it—all of these might indeed be a visualization of Isaiah's "How art thou fallen from heaven, O Lucifer, son of the morning! how art thou cut down to the ground!"

The Lucifer identification also makes understandable the lack of genitals in a figure so powerfully masculine, for even the archangels who are portrayed as being male in mien and gear do not have sexual parts in traditional art.

92. George Inness. *September Afternoon.* 1887. Oil on canvas. 36¾ x 28¾". National Collection of Fine Arts, Smithsonian Institution, Washington, D.C.

George Inness was born in New York state, worked with a map engraver in New York, and then studied briefly with R. F. Gignoux of Brooklyn. He was influenced both by the native Hudson River School landscapists and the Barbizon painters whose works he studied on his third trip to Europe in 1854. He was introduced to Swedenborg by William Page and, as Joshua Taylor notes in his essay, there is speculation as to whether the later paintings of Inness reflect Swedenborgian mystical ideas. Pictorially, a softening of contours and muted range of contrast was seen in American painting from the late 1860s on. But for Inness, as Joshua Taylor notes, "the actual objects of nature become only motifs for the expression of an inner mystery."

George Inness did a number of paintings with overtly religious subject matter, among them a *Triumph of the Cross, or Crucifixion, The Valley of the Shadow of Death,* and a painting listed by Tuckerman as an illustration for *Pilgrim's Progress,* entitled *A Vision of Faith.*

Reference: (1) George Inness, Jr., *The Life, Art and Letters of George Inness,* New York, Century Co., 1917; (2) Le Roy Ireland, *The Works of George Inness,* Austin, University of Texas Press, 1965.

*****93.** Edwin Romanzo Elmer. *Mourning Picture.* (ca. 1889). Oil on canvas. 28 x 36". Smith College Museum of Art, Northampton, Massachusetts. [Dallas and Indianapolis showings only].

At first glance this painting seems a realistic, even photographic rendering of a family scene. Alfred Frankenstein points out that "the little girl...was painted with the lamb to show that she was dead. (How many children's tombstones in old New England graveyards are adorned with the Lamb of God?) This mourning picture, though undated, is said to be one of Elmer's earliest works. The little girl was his own daughter, the man and woman her parents, and the house one which Elmer himself had built."

The artist Edwin Elmer had had no formal art training when *Mourning Picture* was painted, but since his youth had drawn and painted in his spare time. His brother and he, when in their teens, went to Ohio to work in the spool-silk business. They saved their money, returned to their parents in Massachusetts, and decided to build a new home for them, but made it large enough as well for themselves and their prospective brides. The house was patterned after the early Victorian houses they had seen in Cleveland.

This house, which the brothers finished in 1876, is portrayed in the background of the painting. Edwin married, and in 1880 a daughter Effie was born. Effie's death was the occasion for this extraordinary, somber painting.

Reference: (1) Maud Valona Elmer, "Edwin Romanzo Elmer as I Knew Him," *The Massachusetts Review,* Autumn-Winter 1964–1965; (2) Alfred Frankenstein, "Edwin Romanzo Elmer," *Magazine of Art,* October 1952, p.270.

Robert Loftin Newman was born in Richmond, Virginia, in 1827. At the age of ten he was in Clarksville, Tennessee, where despite financial handicaps he somehow managed to develop his talent as a painter. In 1850 and 1854 he was able to make his way to Paris, where he studied briefly under Thomas Couture and met Jean Francois Millet, a painter whose style became a pervasive influence throughout Newman's long life.

During the Civil War Newman served without distinction or conviction in the Confederate army. Stationed at Richmond when the army fell to Grant, he applied for and was granted a Provost Marshal's pass to the North. Except for a few return trips to visit his mother, it marked Newman's final departure from the South.

Little is known of his activities for the next three decades. But in 1894 the Knoedler Gallery in New York and the Boston Museum of Fine Arts gave him a large show of 109 titles. The committee for the exhibition included such distinguished arbiters of taste as the architect Stanford White, the painter William Merritt Chase, the collector John Gellatly. For the next fifteen years sporadic attempts were made to win a wider acceptance for Newman's paintings, but with little success; he died virtually unknown in New York City in 1912, a pauper and almost certainly a suicide. An auction sale of his effects, including several paintings, realized a total of about $85.
Reference: Robert Loftin Newman, Tennessee Fine Arts Center, Nashville, Tennessee.

94. Robert Loftin Newman. *Christ and Peter on the Sea of Galilee.* (n.d.). Oil on canvas. 12¼ x 14¾". Portland Art Museum, Portland, Oregon.

The Biblical episode here represented is a miraculous event which follows upon the Feeding of the 5,000, when Jesus had gone up into the hills to pray: "When evening came, he was there alone, but the boat by this time was out on the sea, beaten by the waves; for the wind was against them. And in the fourth watch of the night he came to them, walking on the sea. But when the disciples saw him walking on the sea, they were terrified, saying, 'It is a ghost!' And they cried out for fear. But immediately he spoke to them, saying, 'Take heart, it is I: have no fear.' And Peter answered him, 'Lord, if it is you, bid me come to you on the water.' He said, 'Come.' So Peter got out of the boat and walked on the water and came to Jesus; but when he saw the wind, he was afraid, and beginning to sink he cried out, 'Lord, save me.' Jesus immediately reached out his hand and caught him" (Matthew 14:25–31).

In Newman's painting the figure of Christ is identified by the nimbus about his head, the only clearly delineated form in the painting. Peter is barely distinguishable. But a supernatural luminosity about the shadowy figures focuses attention on them, and draws them into unity with the sea and sky.

*95. Robert Loftin Newman. *Madonna and Child in a Landscape.* (n.d.). Oil on canvas. 22 x 16″. Tennessee Fine Arts Center, Nashville.

As with the paintings of the Romantic artist, Ryder, Newman's paintings represent the human figure embedded in undefined, mysterious, penumbrous nature. In many of the paintings the natural setting for the figures seems radiant, as in this charming painting. Newman's Madonna turns to one side, her profile merging with the face of the infant Jesus.

Newman is "painterly" in his use of broad strokes of juxtaposed color to build up his forms. Thus in Newman's painting the figure and background together form a unity, nature setting off the mother and the divine child, and participating in the sacred character of the two.

96. Robert Loftin Newman. *Adoration.* (n.d.). Oil on canvas. 8⅞ x 12″. The Brooklyn Museum.

*97. Robert Loftin Newman. *The Good Samaritan.* 1886. Oil on canvas. 9 x 11″. The Newark Museum, Newark, New Jersey.

Newman, in his interpretation of the parable of the Good Samaritan, concentrates the entire meaning of the parable in the two figures, and gives an additional dimension by contrasting age and youth. The man en route to Jericho when he was stripped and beaten by robbers is depicted as a very young man who indeed appears half-dead. The Samaritan is an old man who bends over the victim, embracing him as he gathers his strength to lift him onto his own beast, standing patiently, vigilantly nearby. Nature is so encompassing and vaporous in Newman's painting that the donkey is not readily recognizable, and the exact posture of the traveler and the Samaritan must be puzzled out.

Newman's additions to the Biblical account give it greater complexity of meaning. The parable is told to answer the question: Who is my neighbor? The parable teaches that the neighbor is the outcast and the victim. Newman adds the dimension of youth and age; and nature represented by the Samaritan's beast and the crepuscular, encompassing setting appear to be part of the equation also. It is a painting which invites repeated viewings, illumining understanding of the subject matter but drawing us beyond the implications of the parable.

Albert P. Ryder was a descendant of Cape Cod families, and his paternal grandparents belonged to a strict Methodist sect whose women dressed Quaker fashion. In 1840 the family moved to New Bedford, then the greatest whaling port in the world, and it was there that Albert was born in 1847.

In 1879 the family moved to New York, Ryder's home for the rest of his life. He studied for a time at the National Academy of Design, and also under the portraitist and engraver, William Marshall. His first recorded exhibition at the National Academy was in 1873. In 1877 he went to London for a month and in 1887 and 1896 he crossed and recrossed the Atlantic on a ship captained by a friend of his.

The preceding information is a selection of the facts of Ryder's biography. In the case of this artist, perhaps more than any other included in this exhibition, the facts do not illumine his gifts and his personality. As Barbara Novak observed, Ryder's entire oeuvre, religious or secular, might be seen as an act of devotion. Ryder painted two versions of the Easter morning encounter of Christ with the Magdalene, another version of the *Way of the Cross*, the extraordinary *Jonah* (ill. p.26), and many small seascapes. The latter are the work of a visionary and a romantic, one who sees all of nature within the purview of the Almighty, as is also the case in his *Jonah*.

In studying Ryder's work, it is interesting to discover that the human figure is most fully realized in the paintings with religious subject matter; in the two paintings of Christ and the Magdalene, and the *Joan of Arc*, the figure is larger in scale, and rendered with more detail, and more psychic identity than is the case in his other works. In the filtered daylit or moonlit land- and seascapes (actually the terms land- and seascapes with their suggestion of horizontal extension in space do not seem appropriate for these glimpses of nature distilled by the hand and the spirit of Ryder), the human figures are embedded in nature, their posture and gestures hardly distinguishable from their setting.

Lloyd Goodrich says that Ryder is "one of the few authentic religious painters of his period—in whom religion was not mere conformity, but deep personal emotion. The life of Christ moved him to some of his most tender and impressive works."

Because of Ryder's method of working on his canvases over long periods of time, applying layers of pigment upon earlier coats which were not entirely dry, his paintings are in fragile condition. Many of them can only survive in entirely controlled and stable conditions, and thus some of his most representative religious paintings could not be included in this exhibition. *Reference:* (1) Lloyd Goodrich, *Albert P. Ryder*, New York, George Braziller, Inc., 1959; (2) Barbara Novak, *American Painting of the Nineteenth Century*, New York, Praeger Publishers, 1969.

98. Albert P. Ryder. *The Way of the Cross.* (n.d.). Oil on canvas. 14 x 11". Addison Gallery of American Art, Phillips Academy, Andover, Massachusetts.

Two versions exist of this subject; the present painting was originally acquired along with others from Ryder in his declining years by a woman "as a gift of appreciation and gratitude for friendship." Lloyd Goodrich thought at one time that this painting might have been tampered with, and estimates that Ryder painted about 160 pictures, but probably five times as many are falsely ascribed to him. He notes that Ryder's work has been extensively forged, and speculates that this is due in part to Ryder's small total output. In Ryder's later years, high prices were paid for his work as his reputation grew among collectors. His habit of keeping his paintings "in progress" for long periods of time—years in some cases—and of changing the compositions and adding layers of paint, resulted in far fewer pictures, many of which bear heavy loads of pigment on small canvases.
Reference: Lloyd Goodrich, *Albert P. Ryder,* New York, George Braziller, Inc., 1959.

99. Albert P. Ryder. *Joan of Arc.* (n.d.). Oil on canvas. 10⅛ x 7⅛". Worcester Art Museum, Worcester, Massachusetts: Theodore T. and Mary G. Ellis Collection.

Ryder not only read poetry extensively but wrote it as well. His poems were often visionary and lyric, and some were about his paintings. The first stanza of Ryder's poem about his *Joan of Arc* reads: "On a rude mossy throne / Made by Nature in the stone / Joan sits: and her eyes far away. / Rest upon the mountains gray. / And far beyond the moving clouds / That wrap the sky in vap'rous shrouds, / Visions, she sees— / And voices come to her on the breeze."

The figure of Joan merges with the rude, mossy throne but her upward glance in her still face suggests the quietude of attentive listening. She holds the shepherd's staff in one hand and with the other reaches forward in a gesture which seems at once seeking and harking to other voices. The zone of light about her head is less a halo (as seen in the paintings of Ryder's contemporaries LaFarge and Sargent) than an evidence of the spirit immanent within nature and the young shepherdess.
Reference: Lloyd Goodrich, *Albert P. Ryder,* New York, George Braziller, Inc., 1959.

*100. Thomas Eakins. *Study for the Crucifixion.* (1880). Oil on canvas. 22 x 18". The Hirshhorn Museum and Sculpture Garden, Smithsonian Institution, Washington, D.C.

The sketch for the *Crucifixion* painting has a bold dark-and-light pattern, heavy impasto, and a spontaneous application of paint, all characteristics which distinguish it from the final painting now in the collection of the Philadelphia Museum of Art. Yet the sketch is remarkably crystallized in its design concept. If one compares the contours of the figure and the configuration of the shadows in the *Study* with the final *Crucifixion,* there is a significant similarity.

In 1880 Thomas Eakins painted the life-sized *Crucifixion.* It is unusual in the history of American painting and it stands alone in Eakins' work as well. It is conspicuously large when compared with his other works. There is nothing provisional, sketchy, or exploratory about its conception or execution. The painting is as carefully composed and fully realized as if it had been done for a particular commission. Yet it seems unlikely that it was created for a particular place, and it is quite certain that it was done without reference to any religious body or beliefs. Eakins was an agnostic. Though Eakins had friends on the faculty of the Catholic seminary, St. Charles Borromeo at Overbrook, to whom he loaned the painting of the *Crucifixion* for several years, he was not a member of any church or denomination.

In the large painting Jesus is seen in full, pale sunlight, with a bleak and rocky landscape in the background. The steady fidelity with which Eakins rendered the nude figure and the particularity with which he renders his model command attention. John Laurie Wallace, a student and friend, posed for the painting, according to Margaret McHenry, strapped to a cross which was on the roof of Eakins' third-floor studio.

Reference: (1) Jane Dillenberger, *Secular Art with Sacred Themes,* New York, Abingdon Press, 1969; (2) Evan H. Turner, "Thomas Eakins at Overbrook," *Records of the American Catholic Historical Society of Philadelphia,* Vol. 81, December, 1970, No. 4, p. 195.

Tanner's son wrote, "My father was the son of Benjamin Tucker Tanner, a bishop in the African Methodist Episcopal Church and a fourth-generation American of Negro extraction. But he always felt himself to be an American first and a Negro second. This was quite natural, as our family was of mixed blood with Red Indian, Negro, and white ancestors." Tanner was born in Pittsburgh in 1859, then moved with his family to Philadelphia, where he began his serious study of art. Between 1880–1882 he worked at the Pennsylvania Academy of Fine Arts under Thomas Eakins, a teacher of extraordinary ability, and Professor of Drawing and Painting. Eakins' *Crucifixion* was painted during the period Tanner studied with him, and it would be interesting to know how Tanner viewed this life-sized realistic representation of the Crucifixion event. Tanner apparently never painted the subject, though at the end of his life he did a *Return from the Crucifixion*, showing the three distant crosses and Mary and the disciples on the road leading away from Golgotha.

Tanner taught drawing at Clark University, Atlanta; then in 1891 he went to Paris and studied at the Acadamie Julien, exhibiting at the Salon in 1894. In 1897 his painting *The Raising of Lazarus* was purchased by the French Government for the Luxembourg Gallery. In 1897 and 1898 he went to Palestine. In 1899 he married Jessie Olssen, a white American girl, in London. Awards and honors from both France, Tanner's adopted home, and the United States continued to be given him.

His son wrote of him, "If my father lived so much abroad it was owing to the fact that he felt the white people in America were not ready to face acceptance of the colored races, especially the Negro race. He believed this acceptance would eventually be worked out through education and equal opportunity, though it might take many years.

"In Europe my father was taken for what he was, a talented artist whose 'colour' did not add to or detract from his talent. Not only did he not feel any racial prejudice, but in Europe other Americans acted as though racial prejudice did not exist in their own country."
Reference: Marcia M. Mathews, *Henry Ossawa Tanner, American Artist,* Chicago, 1969.

101. Henry Ossawa Tanner. *The Annunciation.* 1898. Oil on canvas. 57 x 71¼". Lent by the Commissioners of Fairmount Park, W. P. Wilstach Collection, courtesy of the Philadelphia Museum of Art.

102. Henry Ossawa Tanner. *Study for the Annunciation.* (n.d.). Oil tempera on board. 8½ x 10½". Museum of African Art / Frederick Douglass Institute, Washington, D.C.

Tanner made two trips to the Holy Land. According to an entry in his travel notebook in 1897 he "made a trip from Jerusalem to Jericho-Jordan-Dead Sea for 40 frcs." The *Annunciation* was executed after this trip and some of the setting and fabrics may reflect observations made then. But the model for Mary was Jessie Olssen, a young American girl, daughter of a San Franciscan in the shipbuilding industry. Tanner, who was fifteen years her senior, met her at Barbizon in France. They were married in 1899 in London and the *Annunciation* was the first of many paintings for which she posed. The painting was exhibited in the Old Salon in Paris, 1898, and later in Philadelphia, where it was purchased for the Wilstach collection of the Philadelphia Museum.

As Tanner's fame as an artist grew, he was interviewed by Vance Thompson for an article for *Cosmopolitan* on "American Artists in Paris." Reviewing Tanner's successes with the Salon exhibitions, he concluded several paragraphs by the remark: "A strange personnage, this young mulatto (referring to Tanner's mixture of Negro, American Indian, and white ancestry) —the product of Philadelphia and the Latin Quarter and Bethlehem—who is destined, I like to think, to give the world a new conception, at once reverent, critical and visionary, of the scenes of the Bible."

Reference: Marcia M. Mathews, *Henry Ossawa Tanner, American Artist,* Chicago, 1969.

*103. Henry Ossawa Tanner. *The Saviour.* (n.d.). Oil on plywood. 29⅛ x 21⅞". Museum of African Art / Frederick Douglass Institute, Washington, D.C. [Ill. p.31].

The intensity of the emotional power in this spontaneous sketch brings to mind some of Rembrandt's drawings and etchings of Jesus. Reflecting on religious art, Tanner wrote:

> It has very often seemed to me that many painters of religious subjects (in our time) seem to forget that their pictures should be as much works of art (regardless of the subject) as are other paintings with less holy subjects. To suppose that the fact of the religious painter having a more elevated subject than his brother artist makes it unnecessary for him to consider his picture as an artistic production…simply proves that he is less of an artist than he who gives the subject his best attention. Or for him to suppose that his having such a subject can…be construed as an excuse for making a picture in which the literary side shall be its only quality, or in which a so-called religious sentiment will take the place of the qualities loved by artists… is equally false.
>
> I believe most sincerely in a religious sentiment in religious pictures but, so far, have never seen it in a canvas which did not possess also artistic qualities…

Reference: Marcia M. Mathews, *Henry Ossawa Tanner, American Artist,* Chicago, 1969.

*104. Henry Ossawa Tanner. *Two Disciples at the Tomb.* (1906). Oil on canvas. 51 x 41⅞". The Art Institute of Chicago: Robert A. Waller Fund.

Tanner had achieved recognition in French art circles, and had received some attention by the American press when his *Two Disciples at the Tomb* was shown in Paris at the Art Club. Then it received the Harris Prize of $500 for "the most impressive and distinguished work of art of the season" and was acquired for the Chicago Art Institute.

Throughout his career Tanner depicted episodes with an individual interpretation bespeaking his own involvement with the subject matter. Rather than depicting the traditional subject of the Marys at the tomb, he has chosen to represent Simon Peter and John at the tomb of Jesus on Easter morning, as they struggle to understand the evidence of their eyes. The younger disciple, "the one whom Jesus loved," seems about to enter the tomb—it was he who "saw and believed." The older, bearded Peter gazes with a troubled expression, his hands clasped thoughtfully. Tanner, with a fine sense for proportion and balance, has set the two heads in the upper quarter of the canvas, where they command our attention, and dominate the large, undetailed areas of the rest of the canvas.

105. Henry Ossawa Tanner. *Angel Appearing before the Wise Men.* (ca. 1910). Oil on canvas. 24⅝ x 31⅞". Museum of African Art / Frederick Douglass Institute, Washington, D.C.

This scene, with the Wise Men far below along a Palestinian road, is depicted from what might be called an angel's-eye view. One spectral angel, with one hand raised and a nimbus about the head is only partially visible at the left. A phalanx of angels, again somewhat spectral, appear to watch protectively over the progress of the Magi below.

In 1898 Rodman Wannamaker of Philadelphia suggested that Tanner visit the Holy Land again at his expense. Tanner wrote of the experience:

> We spent six months painting around Jerusalem and the Dead Sea, and this gave me an insight into the country and the character of the people that my shorter visit had only whetted my appetite for…Never shall I forget…a ride one stormy Christmas night to Bethlehem. Dark clouds swept the moonlit skies and it took little imagination to close one's eyes to the flight of time and see in those hurrying travelers the crowds that hurried Bethlehemward on the memorable night of the Nativity…

Reference: Marcia M. Mathews, *Henry Ossawa Tanner, American Artist,* Chicago, 1969.

106. Henry Ossawa Tanner. *The Burning of Sodom and Gomorrah.* (n.d.). Oil on panel. 20⅜ x 36". The High Museum of Art, Atlanta, Georgia: J. J. Haverty Collection.

Painted after Tanner's two trips to Palestine, during which he sketched the landscape around Jerusalem and the Dead Sea, this scene depicts the destruction of the two cities of Sodom and Gomorrah "because the outcry against them is great and their sin is very grave…Then the Lord rained on Sodom and Gomorrah brimstone and fire from the Lord out of heaven and he overthrew those cities, and all the valley, and all the inhabitants of the cities, and what grew on the ground" (Genesis 19:24). The small group in the right middle ground are Lot and his daughters being led to safety by two angels.

107. Henry Ossawa Tanner. *Moses in the Bullrushes.* (1921). Oil on wood panel. 22¼ x 15¼". Museum of African Art / Frederick Douglass Institute, Washington, D.C.

"Now the daughter of Pharaoh came down to bathe at the river, and her maidens walked beside the river: she saw the basket among the reeds and sent her maid to fetch it. When she opened it she saw the child; and lo, the babe was crying. She took pity on him and said, 'This is one of the Hebrew's children.'" This "goodly child" was brought up by Pharaoh's daughter "and she named him Moses for she said, 'Because I drew him out of the water'" (Exodus 2:5 ff).

The account of the finding of Moses exercised a particular attraction for eighteenth- and nineteenth-century artists; many paintings of the subject exist, by professional as well as naive artists.

The date of this work, which falls well within the twentieth century, is beyond the definition of the exhibition. But stylistically it belongs in the present selection with Tanner's other religious works.

108. Henry Ossawa Tanner. *Daniel in the Lions' Den.* (ca. 1916). Oil on paper on canvas. 41¼ x 50". Los Angeles County Museum of Art: Mr. and Mrs. William Preston Harrison Collection.

Tanner went to Paris in 1891 to study art. In 1894 and 1895 he had paintings accepted at the Paris Salon, and in 1896 his *Daniel in the Lions' Den* received an honorable mention. The United Press correspondent who wrote a report on the Salon exhibition noted that "H. O. Tanner, whose *Young Sabot Maker* elicited so much admiration last year, is again to the front with a large canvas representing *Daniel in the Lions' Den.*"

The original painting of this subject was done by Tanner in 1896; the curators of the Los Angeles County Museum now believe this painting is the third copy of the original and was painted around 1916.

John LaFarge was born in New York City, the son of prosperous French emigres, his father having been a refugee from the ill-fated Napoleonic expedition to San Domingo. LaFarge began drawing at an early age, had intermittent instruction, and graduated from the Roman Catholic Mount St. Mary's College in Maryland. In 1856 he went to Europe, worked briefly under the painter Thomas Couture in Paris, and traveled in northern Europe. Returning to the United States, he went to Newport in order to study with William Morris Hunt. There he met William and Henry James (William James was then also a student of Hunt's).

LaFarge was one of the first American artists to import and be influenced by Japanese color prints (1863). He made a trip to Japan with Henry Adams in 1886, later publishing *An Artist's Letters from Japan* (1897).

In 1876 LaFarge completed a whole complex of mural decorations for Richardson's distinguished Trinity Church in Copley Square, Boston; it was his first large-scale commission. H. H. Richardson won the architectural competition for the New Trinity; he and LaFarge had been friends for some time. LaFarge wrote of Trinity, "I was able to propose to Richardson to change entirely the character of his building…I brought him photographs of the Spanish Romanesque churches, Avila and so forth…It was thus that I came to decorate Trinity Church, Boston, which was being built by my friend Richardson, who believed in me without having much proof of what I could do in that way."

LaFarge was responsible for the entire decorative scheme of the nave and apse, which included many subjects from the Old and New Testaments. High on the nave walls on either side are two immense paintings, *Christ and the Woman of Samaria at the Well,* and *Christ and Nicodemus.* LaFarge's Trinity paintings were executed in an extraordinarily short time, with the help of assistants. Their surface and texture cannot be appreciated because of the low-key tonality, distance, and dimness. But the oil painting of this subject in this exhibition (ill. p.165) shows the subtly vibrant color and beauty of brushwork of LaFarge's own hand. The wall paintings of Trinity depart from the traditional iconographic subjects in the rest of the church, dealing with quiet conversation resulting in a moment of illumination, rather than focusing on an event.

LaFarge worked out a technique for creating opalescent glass, and had many commissions from churches and private patrons for stained glass windows. Some of the important commissions were for windows at Trinity Church, Boston; Memorial Hall at Harvard; the Church of the Incarnation and the Paulist Church, New York City. But alongside these commissions, LaFarge continued to paint and accept mural commissions. Perhaps the best known of the latter is the great apse mural of the Ascension of Christ in the Church of the Ascension in New York City, completed in 1887.

By birth, upbringing and style of life, John LaFarge was a cosmopolite. The evidence of his own contemporaries is that he exercised a considerable personal magnetism. Elihu Vedder, who was only a year younger than LaFarge, found him inspiring, and looked to LaFarge as one of the few whose approval he valued. Vedder admired in LaFarge's paintings "his striving to express shades of thought so delicate that they seem to render words almost useless."

Reference: (1) Royal Cortissoz, *John LaFarge,* Boston, 1911;
(2) Regina Soria, *Elihu Vedder, American Visionary Artist in Rome,* Rutherford, New Jersey, 1970.

109. John LaFarge. *Visit of Nicodemus to Christ.* (ca. 1870–1880). Oil on canvas. 41¾ x 35″. National Collection of Fine Arts, Smithsonian Institution, Washington, D.C.

This painting focuses upon the perplexed, old Nicodemus who gestures as he asks, "How can a man be born when he is old? Can he enter a second time into his mother's womb and be born?" Jesus replied, "…unless one is born of water and the Spirit, he cannot enter the kingdom of God."

The subject must have had a special meaning for LaFarge, since several drawings of it exist, and the design was also adapted for stained glass by him. The first painting of the subject was the mural for Trinity Church, and the painting here is a subsequent oil rendering of the same composition. *Reference:* Royal Cortissoz, *John LaFarge,* Boston, 1911.

110. John LaFarge. *Sketch, Ames Memorial Window.* (n.d.). Watercolor. 17-15/16 x 11-1/2″. Fogg Art Museum, Harvard University, Cambridge, Massachusetts: Louise E. Bettens Fund.

This working drawing shows one phase in the development of the design for a large stained glass window for North Easton, Massachusetts. The three figures in the lower zone of the design are based upon the famous classical relief, the so-called Boston throne, in the Museum of Fine Arts in Boston. As is the case in the study for the *American Madonna,* LaFarge, with conscious eclecticism, has appropriated a motif from an earlier work of art, and made it his own by transformations in the iconography and style. The color scheme is still in process of definition. LaFarge did not entrust the execution to craftsmen alone, but chose the pieces of glass for the window himself. He had discovered how to make opalescent glass, which he used along with many other kinds—translucent, transparent, and even textured glass with surfaces specifically molded for special effects.

111. John LaFarge. *Two Saints* (n.d.). Watercolor and crayon on paper mounted on panel. Each, 24¼ x 19⅜″. Dallas Museum of Fine Arts. [One illustrated].

This pair of female saints appears to be cartoons for a wall painting, or for stained glass windows. They have not yet been identified with a particular commission. The French government bestowed the insignia of the Legion of Honor upon LaFarge when he exhibited one of his windows at the Paris Exposition in 1889. LaFarge's biographer recounts that he made several thousand windows of all sizes and dimensions, most of these for churches. Memorial Hall at Harvard, Trinity Church at Boston, the Church of the Incarnation and the Church of the Assumption in New York City, represent a few of these.

112. John LaFarge. *Study for the "American Madonna," Emmanuel Chapel, St. Luke's Cathedral, Portland, Maine.* (ca. 1904). Charcoal on thin oriental paper. 11 x 7-15/16". The Toledo Museum of Art: Gift of Edward Drummond Libbey.

This is a preliminary study for a mural painted on canvas for Emmanuel Chapel, St. Luke's Cathedral, Portland, Maine. It is based on Raphael's *Sistine Madonna.* While the posture of the Madonna is similar to that depicted by Raphael, the posture of the Christ Child differs notably from it. The Child is older, and His right hand is raised in a conscious gesture of blessing.

It is a beautiful drawing, showing the same delicacy yet sureness of touch which characterizes the painting of *Nicodemus and Christ.* The features of both the Madonna and Child are suggested through subtle gradations of tone. These contrast with such areas as the folds of the robe of the Madonna over the shoulder and across her left arm which are delineated with such a fine precision of draftsmanship.

Born in New York City, Elihu Vedder, a descendant of Dutch forebears who had settled in this land before 1657, had his early education in New York City and Long Island. He started drawing in his youth, selling his first painting at the age of nineteen. Apparently his education was sound for though Vedder never went to college, his knowledge of humanistic studies was wide; all his life he had writers, intellectuals, poets, and artists as his friends. His mother encouraged him in his wish to be an artist and early in 1851 he began lessons with a drawing master, later entering the studio of an artist in Shelburne, New York. In 1856 Vedder embarked for Europe, and later in Florence studied with a copyist and teacher, Bonaiuti, who revered antiquity and taught Vedder draftsmanship.

Vedder returned to the States a number of times, but for the rest of his life his home was Rome, where he was at the center of the comings and goings of artists and poets of many countries who came for the city itself as well as for each other's company.

Vedder's mother was a Universalist, holding with serene conviction that there was no judgment and no place of eternal punishment. Nonetheless, in later years Vedder remarked that "in those early days no Christian home was complete without a Hell." Regina Soria remarked that his whole life was a struggle between faith and doubt. In his autobiographical *Digressions of 'V',* he said of himself, "I am not a mystic, but I have a strong tendency to conjure up visions and to see in things more than meets the eye." In reading Vedder's letters and the family documents as well as the *Digressions,* his personality emerges as a compound of extroverted vigor, volatility, jocularity, and flirtatiousness, with an introverted fascination with dreams, a preoccupation with death, a tendency toward melancholia, and an appetite for the macabre. Indeed, among his confreres the word "veddersque" emerged as a term for that which is weird. In later years he was absorbed in Buddhism and theosophy.
Reference: Regina Soria, *Elihu Vedder: American Visionary Artist in Rome,* Rutherford, New Jersey, 1970.

113. Elihu Vedder. *Star of Bethlehem.* (n.d.). Oil on canvas. 10½ x 12⅝". J. B. Speed Art Museum, Louisville, Kentucky.

The initial version of the *Star of Bethlehem* was exhibited in the National Academy spring exhibition of 1863. A contemporary critic commented that the artist is a "man who could think high thoughts and give expression to them . . . a newcomer who would have something better to show us than watermelons, dogs, and bears, and unreal mountains . . ."

Vedder did a similar painting in 1879, and described it in a letter as a "grand conception!" What he said of the second painting is equally true of this one: "Over a landscape (in which the desert is represented with his usual truth) go the magi . . . A shadowy circle of cloud figures are grouped about a brilliant light in their center, from which a stream of fiery vapor descends straight down the plain to indicate the spot where Christ was born."

Reference: Regina Soria, *Elihu Vedder: American Visionary Artist in Rome,* Rutherford, New Jersey, 1970.

*114. Elihu Vedder. *The Cup of Death.* 1885 and 1911. Oil on canvas. 44¾ x 22¼". National Collection of Fine Arts, Smithsonian Institution, Washington, D.C.

This is the first of two paintings, both of which closely follow Vedder's illustration for a quatrain of the *Rubaiyat of Omar Khayyam:* "So when the Angel of the darker Drink / At last shall find you by the river-brink, / And, offering his Cup, invite your Soul / Forth to your Lips to quaff—you shall not shrink."

Edward FitzGerald's translation of the Persian poem, first published in 1858, was followed by many later editions. It soon became the object of an American cult. Vedder did fifty-six designs for the first American edition of *The Rubaiyat,* a handsome volume published by Houghton Mifflin.

Many of Vedder's Omar Khayyam drawings incorporate imagery and symbols of Christian iconography: *The Last Man* becomes an Adam with the serpent whispering in his ear; a nude figure weeping is a repentant Magdalene identified by her attribute, the ointment jar at her feet.

Vedder's daughter recalled that *The Cup of Death* remained unfinished for some time, because its somber color displeased Vedder. So he laid out a second version in richer colors. The second version was purchased by Miss Susan Mims of Boston, "whose fad is to have the greatest collection of 'dances of death' going," Vedder wrote, adding, "Well, all I can say is 'Viva la faccia of death . . .'"

When Miss Mims died, Vedder's daughter remarked "I do not know what has become of her collection of representations of Death. Certainly my father represents it in a consoling and fortifying manner so that even a dying person could gaze with pleasure on it." His daughter further reported that when the Vedders moved, the unfinished first version was so favorably re-hung that Vedder was drawn back to it, finishing it with pleasure. It is this painting of *The Cup of Death* which is here exhibited.

Reference: Regina Soria, *Elihu Vedder: American Visionary Artist in Rome,* Rutherford, New Jersey, 1970.

*115. Elihu Vedder. *The Soul between Doubt and Faith.* (1899). Oil on canvas. 16½ x 23". The Baltimore Museum of Art.

The motto in the border along the lower edge of the canvas identifies the heads from left to right as *Doubt, Soul,* and *Faith.* Three other versions of this subject existed, the first done in 1886, soon after and perhaps influenced by, the Rubaiyat designs. A color plate of the painting in the exhibition is used as the frontispiece for Vedder's *Doubt and Other Things,* a volume of his poems which are not distinguished as literature but are fascinating for the articulate and candid way that Vedder argues, laughs, despairs, doubts, and hopes in regard to the eternal questions of life and death, faith and doubt, art and nothingness.

A statement from an old exhibition catalogue is pasted on the back of the painting, its original source being an article published in *The Atlantic Monthly,* June 1887, by W. H. Downes, who appraises the painting thus: ". . . the delineation of a psychological mood is a triumph of expression. Into these haggard features Vedder has poured a world of mournful meaning which touches the heart, and moves it to pity for poor humanity thus typified."

116. Elihu Vedder. *Study for the Head of Lazarus.* (n.d.). Oil on canvas. 7⅞ x 9⅝". J. B. Speed Art Museum, Louisville, Kentucky.

This earlier study for Lazarus has a freedom of brushwork and the power of a composition committed to canvas while the original conception was fresh and immediate. By contrast, the later Boston version is more finished, with greater detail in the grave cloths and in the rocky background. The result is a sharper focus on Lazarus, since contrasts have been heightened and the onlookers eliminated. However, the earlier Louisville version gains by the extraordinary complexity and power of Lazarus' expression—a haunting face in which dread seems to dominate expectation. We are reminded of the medieval stories about Lazarus which tell of his terror at his own resurrection, associated as it is with the certain knowledge of dying again.

*117. Elihu Vedder. *Lazarus Rising from the Tomb.* 1899. Oil on canvas. 20 x 31½". Museum of Fine Arts, Boston: Gift of Edwin Atkins Grozier.

Vedder declared this to be one of his favorite paintings. In addition to the Louisville study, other drawings and versions of this subject are known to have been painted by Vedder. In this painting, rather than depicting the drama of the event as in Renaissance art, Vedder focuses upon the resurrected Lazarus at the moment when life and thought return. He is still physically and in part psychically within the cave which formed the tomb, his face in shadow except for a touch of light along the bridge of the nose, lip, and chin. The handsome Mediterranean features of this Lazarus have a sadness and stillness to them. He seems not to embrace returning life but passively accepts it.

118. Elihu Vedder. *The Ninth Hour: Crucifixion.* (n.d.). Oil on canvas mounted on panel. 9½ x 8½". Kennedy Galleries, Inc., New York.

Early in his career Vedder planned a cycle of paintings on the life of Christ. Those which have been located are mainly on the theme of the Crucifixion. There are two other existing versions of the painting in this exhibition; another called *The Eleventh Hour,* two of the Descent from the Cross, one Mocking of Christ, and at least two oil sketches of the Crown of Thorns. On the back of one of these latter is Vedder's sketch for a triptych of saints or apostles. In view of his Universalist religious background, the emphasis in his work upon Passion subjects suggests a personal identification with the theme of Jesus' suffering.

Vedder has shown the Ninth Hour through the eyes of the bystanders; the women, Mary among them, turn away mutely at Jesus' last cry. An elderly follower, perhaps Nicodemus, painedly and numbly stares at the man who turns and points to the three crosses, wondering if Elijah will come to save Jesus. Though a tiny painting, the repeated verticals of the garments of the shrouded foreground figures give it large rhythms, the somber throb of a threnody.

*119. Moses J. Ezekiel. *Ecce Homo.* (ca. 1899). Bronze. 21-5/8 x 17-13/16 x 16-11/16". Cincinnati Art Museum.

Well known in his own day, Moses Jacob Ezekiel executed important commissions and was the first Jewish artist to be knighted by an Italian king and a German emperor. Leaving his home in Cincinnati in 1869, he studied in Germany and later in Rome, where he converted some of the ruins of the Baths of Diocletian into a studio, in which artists, writers, musicians, and even kings and nobles gathered. He did a few fine portraits, and several large and rather dryly academic commissions of religious subjects. His large bas-relief, *Israel,* incorporates a figure of Christ, unusual in Christian iconography, but not unrelated to this bronze *Ecce Homo.* The conception for the sculpture *Israel* is "Israel as the suffering Messiah, the crucified people, symbolized in terms of the crucified Christ."

Moses Ezekiel himself spoke of his sculpture and his Jewish origin in this vein:

> I must acknowledge that the tendency of the Israelites to stamp everything they undertake with such an emphasis is not sympathetic with my tastes. Artists belong to no country and to no sect—their individual religious opinions are matters of conscience and belong to their households and not to the public. In reference to myself, this is my standpoint. Everybody who knows me knows that I am a Jew—I never wanted it otherwise. But I would prefer as an artist to gain first a name and reputation upon an equal footing with all others in art circles. It is a matter of absolute indifference to the world whether a *good artist* is a Jew or a Gentile and in my career I do not want to be stamped with the title of "Jewish sculptor."

Reference: Joseph Gutmann, "Jewish Participation in the Visual Arts in Eighteenth- and Nineteenth-Century America," *American Jewish Archives,* 15 (April, 1963): 21-57, p. 43.

*120. Abbott H. Thayer. *Virgin Enthroned.* (1891). Oil on canvas. 70¾ x 51″. National Collection of Fine Arts, Smithsonian Institution, Washington, D.C.

Abbott Thayer was born in Boston and brought up in New Hampshire. His training included study at the Brooklyn Art School, the National Academy of Design, and the Ecole des Beaux Arts in Paris. His early paintings are pictures of animals, but he soon turned to portraits, figure paintings, and a few landscape paintings. He opened a studio in New York City in 1879.

In addition to the categories noted above, Thayer painted arresting works with religious subjects—a number of large paintings of angels, and the Freer Collection *Virgin* who strides through flowered fields holding by hand two story-book children. In the *Virgin Enthroned,* in this exhibition, as well as in many other of his pictures, the artist's own children, Mary, Gerald, and Gladys, were the models for the idealized figures.

Thayer said, "Few people understand what they should mean by idealization…art is a record of worship, alias love… what makes a work of art [is] this mark of sacrificing [intuitively] the realness of certain details to that of the loved ones." *Reference: Highlights of the National Collection of Fine Arts,* Washington, D.C., 1968.

Oddly enough, the brilliant and successful portrait painter, John Singer Sargent, was responsible for the largest cycle of murals with religious subject matter in this country. These paintings are, surprisingly, not in a church, but in the Boston Public Library.

McKim, Meade, and White were the architects for the new library to be built in Boston on Copley Square. Although Stanford White wished to have European artists undertake the decoration of the building, the sculptor Augustus Saint-Gaudens insisted that there were "strong men of American fiber who should be employed." He and McKim and White agreed with Charles Moore, who saw "the possibilites opening before them for the creation of the greatest combined work of the architect, painter, and sculptor ever achieved in America up to that time." The French artist, Puvis de Chavannes decorated the central staircase, but Edwin A. Abbey and John Singer Sargent were brought in for major commissions; Sargent was asked to decorate the great vaulted gallery on the third floor.

Sargent was then in his thirties. He had been born in Florence of American parents and was twenty before coming to the United States and thirty-one before visiting Boston. Although London was his home after 1885, he had many American connections and friends, among them Henry James. By the time he received the commission for the Boston Public Library, he was a successful portrait painter. Although he did portrait commissions during the next twenty-six years, his major work was the murals for the third floor hall of the library, a vaulted corridor 84 feet long, 23 feet wide, and 26 feet high. For this area he painted over twenty major large compositions with many additional appended smaller ones. It is known that he originally intended to paint subjects from Spanish literature. How and why he changed to the grandiose theme, *The Development of Religious Thought from Paganism to Christianity,* is not clear from currently available information.

The paintings were done in England, where he and Abbey had a large studio constructed on the grounds of Morgan Hall. They were painted on canvas and shipped to Boston. Sargent worked out a way of combining plaster reliefs with the canvas murals, giving variation to the flat surfaces by introducing three-dimensional ones in details such as the gold-covered halos, candelabra, and angels' wings, and major sculptures such as the *Crucifix* (ill. p.181).
Reference: Walter Muir Whitehill, "The Making of an Architectural Masterpiece, The Boston Public Library," in *The American Art Journal,* Vol II, No. 2, Fall 1970.

121. John Singer Sargent. *Sketch for Frieze of the Prophets.* (Completed in 1919). Oil on canvas. 22 x 28". Museum of Fine Arts, Boston: Gift of Mrs. Francis Ormand.

This oil sketch has the spontaneity and brilliance of Sargent's finest portraits. It shows him working out visual ideas with quick notations of dark and light patterns and by preliminary experiments with posture and gesture. By contrast, the final painting of the frieze of the prophets in the Boston Public Library is somber, majestic, and almost static. In preparation for the Boston murals, Sargent had traveled in the Mediterranean countries and made oil and watercolor studies of Byzantine and early Christian mosaics. The hieratic character of these works of art influenced his style in these library murals.

Sargent selected nineteen prophets to represent in a frieze which ran beneath the large lunette showing the children of Israel beneath the yoke of their oppressors, the Egyptian Pharaoh and the Assyrian King. But the frieze of the prophets was one of the most popular paintings of the entire cycle. Sepia and hand-colored photographs of the major subjects were made by a Boston publisher and were sold in large numbers, disseminating the compositions to many who never saw the original murals.

The plate in this catalogue is made from a photograph taken before the installation of the vault paintings of the Fifteen Mysteries which now surround the lunette at this end of Sargent's hall in the Boston Public Library. Referred to as the Christian murals, this lunette is balanced at the other end of the hall by murals devoted to the Hebraic motifs of which the *Frieze of the Prophets* is a part.

In the upper zone of the mural we see the Trinity with a Byzantine reference, depicted as three persons united by a single, vast enveloping robe. Sargent made their faces in relief from the same mold. In the lower zone angels hold the Instruments of the Passion—the sponge, the reed, the nails, the spear, the crown of thorns, and so forth.

Uniting the two zones is the cross with its figure of the dying Christ, and Adam and Eve, typifying humanity, kneeling at either side. Bound to the body of Christ, they hold chalices to receive his blood. The Latin inscription above the cross reads: "The sins of the world have been forgiven." The inscription on the frieze reads: "I, God in the flesh, man's maker and redeemer, myself made man, redeem both body and soul." Sargent derived this from the inscription in the Cathedral of Cefalu, Sicily (A.D. 1148), but substituted the word "redimo" for "judico."

Reference: (1) *The Handbook of the Boston Public Library,* 1921. Note: pages 37 to 58 describe the Sargent Hall murals and reliefs; (2) David McKibbin, *Sargent's Boston,* Boston, 1956.

*122. John Singer Sargent. *Crucifix for Dogma of the Redemption.* (1900). Bronze. 29 x 20½ x 3". The Hirshhorn Museum and Sculpture Garden, Smithsonian Institution, Washington, D.C. [Berkeley and Washington showings only].

This relief is one of at least two bronze versions Sargent made after the *Crucifix* of the central part of the Redemption mural at the Boston Public Library. On a Byzantine cross the dying Christ hangs between the crouching figures of Adam and Eve, who are bound to the cross of salvation by a wide band. At the foot of the cross, entwining Christ's feet, is the Serpent of Eden, symbol of an old liturgy that refers to Satan "victorious on the tree, he was overcome on the tree." Sargent makes this explicit by showing the nail fastening Christ's feet to the cross also penetrating the Serpent's head. At the foot of the cross the pelican feeds its young with blood from its breast, an ancient symbol of the Resurrection.

The bronze version differs in important details from the *Crucifix* of the library mural. In that version Christ's head is encircled by a halo, and the words "Remissa Sunt Peccata Mundi" appear above the crossbeam. In the Hirshhorn *Crucifix* only a formalized pattern of grapevines is present. The Adam of the bronze *Crucifix* is youthful, while Adam of the mural is bearded, worn, and troubled; the Serpent is twined about his feet, as well as Christ's in the Boston *Crucifix*. The bronze pelican is symmetrical, in contrast to the vigorous asymmetry of this symbolic group in the Boston *Crucifix.*

These differences produce a more doctrinal and liturgical image in the Boston Public Library *Crucifix* than in the bronze. One of the bronze *Crucifixes* hangs in the crypt of St. Paul's Cathedral in London, the city which was Sargent's home for so many years.

*123. Tiffany Studios. *St. Gabriel (Benjamin Harrison Memorial Window)*. (1905). Stained glass. First Presbyterian Church, Indianapolis, Indiana (on extended loan to the Indianapolis Museum of Art). [Indianapolis showing only].

The focus of the large Tiffany window, originally in the First Presbyterian Church in Indianapolis, is the figure of Gabriel, the Angel of the Resurrection. Mrs. Benjamin Harrison commissioned the window in memory of her husband who had been the twenty-third President of the United States and an elder in the church for over forty years. In recent years with the shifting of urban population the church vacated the structure; the memorial window was removed and will be installed in the Indianapolis Museum of Art.

The Archangel Gabriel is seen with the star of the morning above, holding his unfurled trumpet in hand. The inscription in the adjacent panels reads: "Awake thou that sleepest, arise from the dead, and Christ shall give thee light."

184

Index to Artists and Titles
Credits

Artists are indexed alphabetically; the first number is the page on which the catalogue entry appears; the second number, in italics, is the page on which an illustration appears.

Bultos and Retablos

John Bransten, San Francisco
Mr. and Mrs. W. B. Carnochan, Atherton, California
Mr. and Mrs. Richard Manney, Irvington, New York
Mr. and Mrs. Nathan Oliveira, Palo Alto, California
Herbert W. Plimpton, Boston

Addison Gallery of American Art, Phillips Academy, Andover,
    Massachusetts
Albany Institute of History and Art, Albany, New York
Amherst College (Mead Art Building), Amherst, Massachusetts
The Baltimore Museum of Art
Boston Athenaeum
Museum of Fine Arts, Boston
Boston Public Library
The Brooklyn Museum
The Art Institute of Chicago
Cincinnati Art Museum
Cleveland Museum of Art
Dallas Museum of Fine Arts
M. H. deYoung Memorial Museum, San Francisco
Museum of African Art / Frederick Douglass Institute,
    Washington, D.C.
Galerie St. Etienne, New York
Fogg Art Museum, Harvard University, Cambridge,
    Massachusetts
Washington County Museum of Fine Arts, Hagerstown,
    Maryland
The High Museum of Art, Atlanta, Georgia
The Hirshhorn Museum and Sculpture Garden, Smithsonian
    Institution, Washington, D.C.
The Museum of Fine Arts, Houston
Kennedy Galleries, Inc., New York
Los Angeles County Museum of Art
The Moravian Historical Society, Nazareth, Pennsylvania
Tennessee Fine Arts Center, Nashville
The Newark Museum, Newark, New Jersey
The Metropolitan Museum of Art, New York
Pennsylvania Academy of the Fine Arts, Philadelphia

Philadelphia Museum of Art
Portland Art Museum, Portland, Oregon
Abby Aldrich Rockefeller Folk Art Collection, Williamsburg,
    Virginia
Museum of New Mexico, Santa Fe
Washington University Gallery of Art, St. Louis, Missouri
Smith College Museum of Art, Northampton, Massachusetts
J. B. Speed Art Museum, Louisville, Kentucky
Museum of Fine Arts, Springfield, Massachusetts
Friends Historical Library of Swarthmore College, Swarthmore,
    Pennsylvania
The Taylor Museum of the Colorado Springs Fine Arts Center
The Toledo Museum of Art
Wadsworth Atheneum, Hartford, Connecticut
Library of Congress (Prints and Photographs Division),
    Washington, D.C.
National Collection of Fine Arts, Smithsonian Institution,
    Washington, D.C.
National Gallery of Art, Washington, D.C.
Whitney Museum of American Art, New York
Worcester Art Museum, Worcester, Massachusetts
Yale University Art Gallery, New Haven, Connecticut
Brigham Young University Art Collection, Provo, Utah

Photography Credits

Except as here noted, photographs were supplied by courtesy of individual collectors or institutions without specified photographic credit.

W. L. Bowers, #67
George M. Cushing, Boston, #27
O. E. Nelson, New York, #100 (and cover)
Piaget, St. Louis, #87
Eric Pollitzer, New York, #109
Kenneth Schar, Santa Fe, #61
Joseph Szaszfai, Yale University Art Gallery, #20
Mr. and Mrs. Norman Robbins, Frederick Douglass Institute, #103
A. J. Wyatt, Philadelphia, #45, #83

7,500 copies. Book design by Bruce Montgomery. Typography, set in Palatino regular and semibold, by Spartan Typographers. Offset lithography by Cardinal Penn Litho. Plates are printed in 200 line screens with varnish overprinting. Paper is Karma Text, basis 80, and Kromekote, 10pt. cover.